FACING
SERIOUS MENTAL ILLNESS

A Guide for Patients and Their Families

AUTHORS

Oliver Freudenreich, MD

Corinne Cather, PhD

Theodore A. Stern, MD

FACING
SERIOUS MENTAL ILLNESS

A Guide for Patients and Their Families

Facing Serious Mental Illness – A Guide for Patients and Their Families

ISBN-13: 978-1-951166-35-9 (Print)
ISBN-13: 978-1-951166-36-6 (eBook)

Cover Design: Falcone Creative Design, LLC
Book Design: Dianne Russell, Octal Productions, LLC
Book Production: Octal Productions, LLC
Managing Director: Jane Pimental, MGH Psychiatry Academy
Program Manager: Heather Giza, MGH Psychiatry Academy
Administrative Coordinator: Alexandra D. Fowler, MGH Psychiatry Academy
Printing and Binding: RP Graphics
This book is printed on acid-free paper.

ABOUT THE AUTHORS

 Oliver Freudenreich, MD is an Associate Professor of Psychiatry at Harvard Medical School and a Psychiatrist at Massachusetts General Hospital (MGH), serves as co-director of the MGH Schizophrenia Clinical and Research Program and directs the MGH Fellowship in Public and Community Psychiatry. His academic interest lies in the area of optimal psychopharmacological treatment for schizophrenia, including the development of innovative treatments and management of treatment-resistant psychosis. In addition to his clinical and clinical trial expertise in schizophrenia, Dr. Freudenreich provides psychiatric consultations for medically complex patients with serious mental illness and for diagnostically difficult cases with psychosis. He has published extensively in his areas of interest and has written a handbook on psychotic disorders; its second edition was published in 2020. Dr. Freudenreich speaks on a regular basis at international and national meetings.

 Corinne Cather, PhD is an Associate Professor of Psychology at Harvard Medical School and a psychologist at the Massachusetts General Hospital (MGH), serves as the Director of the MGH Center of Excellence for Psychosocial and Systemic Research and directs Psychological Services of the MGH Schizophrenia Program. She is a licensed clinical psychologist with a diplomate in cognitive-behavioral therapy (CBT) from the Academy of Cognitive Therapy. Dr. Cather is a researcher, clinician, and expert trainer. Her research centers on the design and implementation of evidence-based psychosocial treatments for people with first-episode psychosis as well as those with longer histories of serious mental illness (SMI). A focus of her research has been on the development and training of CBT-based health interventions to reduce cardiovascular disease among people with SMI. As a clinician, she provides therapy to individuals and families in the MGH First Episode and Early Psychosis Program. She has trained clinicians across the country who care for people with schizophrenia and is an expert trainer for the NAVIGATE coordinated specialty care model for first-episode psychosis.

Theodore A. Stern, MD is the Ned H. Cassem Professor of Psychiatry in the field of Psychosomatic Medicine/Consultation, Harvard Medical School and Chief Emeritus of the Avery D. Weisman Psychiatry Consultation Service, and Director of the Thomas P. Hackett Center for Scholarship in Psychosomatic Medicine, at the Massachusetts General Hospital in Boston, Massachusetts. Dr. Stern has written more than 450 scientific articles and book chapters and edited more than 40 books, including the *Massachusetts General Hospital Handbook of General Hospital Psychiatry* (4/e–7/e), *Massachusetts General Hospital Comprehensive Clinical Psychiatry* (1/e, 2/e), *Massachusetts General Hospital Guide to Primary Care Psychiatry* (1/e, 2/e), *Massachusetts General Hospital Psychiatry Update and Board Preparation* (1/e–4/e), and *Facing Cancer, Facing Heart Disease, Facing Diabetes, Facing Rheumatoid Arthritis, Facing Immunotherapy, Facing Lupus, Facing Osteoporosis, Facing Scleroderma, Facing Psoriasis, Facing Eczema, Facing Vitiligo, Facing Acne, Facing Burns and Scars, Facing Transplantation, Facing Postoperative Pain, Facing Pelvic Pain, Facing Overweight and Obesity, Facing COVID-19, Facing Cystic Fibrosis*, and *Facing Memory Loss and Dementia*. He is also the Editor-in-Chief Emeritus of *Psychosomatics*.

DEDICATION

To our patients facing serious mental illness,
their families, our students, our colleagues,
our mentors, and our families ...

OF
CC
TAS

ACKNOWLEDGMENTS

OUR THANKS

This book would not have come into being if not for our many patients who expressed their need for a guide to the experience of serious mental illness. They were unfailingly generous in including us in their day-to-day triumphs and struggles. We hope that, through this book, we are fulfilling that need and have done justice to their faith and trust in us.

Without the contributions of so many physicians and related health care professionals, this book would have never been completed. We also thank our teachers and mentors for imbuing in us a sense of responsibility to educate, to write with rigor, and, above all, to provide exceptional care to our patients. In addition, we are grateful to a host of families who have supported our educational efforts through generous donations for many years. Moreover, our efforts have been greatly facilitated by the clinical support provided by our long-standing community partner, the North Suffolk Mental Health Association.

At the Massachusetts General Hospital Psychiatry Academy, we thank Jane Pimental our managing director, Heather Giza our program manager, and administrative coordinator Alexandra D. Fowler, for their assistance and support. At Octal Productions, LLC, our thanks go to Dianne Russell for overseeing the production of this book with grace and style.

OF
CC
TAS

TABLE OF CONTENTS

CHAPTER 3

What Makes Diagnosing Serious Mental Illness Important? 23

Oliver Freudenreich, MD; Corinne Cather, PhD; and Theodore A. Stern, MD

CHAPTER 4

What Are the Goals of Psychiatric Treatment?.. 37

Oliver Freudenreich, MD; Corinne Cather, PhD; and Theodore A. Stern, MD

CHAPTER 5
What Types of Psychiatric Medications Should I Consider? 47
Oliver Freudenreich, MD; Corinne Cather, PhD; and Theodore A. Stern, MD

CHAPTER 6
What Types of Talk Therapies (Psychotherapy) Are There? 61
Corinne Cather, PhD; Oliver Freudenreich, MD; and Theodore A. Stern, MD

CHAPTER 9

CHAPTER 10

CHAPTER 11

CHAPTER 12
Can I Be Hopeful About Recovery?.. 143
Oliver Freudenreich, MD; Corinne Cather, PhD; and Theodore A. Stern, MD

CONTRIBUTORS

Corinne Cather, PhD
Associate Professor of Psychology in
the Department of Psychiatry,
Harvard Medical School;
Director, MGH Center of Excellence for
Psychosocial and Systemic Research,
Director, Psychological Services,
MGH Schizophrenia Program,
Massachusetts General Hospital;
Boston, MA

Oliver Freudenreich, MD
Co-Director, MGH Schizophrenia Clinical
and Research Program,
Director, MGH Fellowship in Public and
Community Psychiatry,
Massachusetts General Hospital;
Associate Professor of Psychiatry,
Harvard Medical School;
Boston, MA

Theodore A. Stern, MD
Ned H. Cassem Professor of Psychiatry in the
field of Psychosomatic Medicine/Consultation,
Harvard Medical School;
Chief Emeritus, Avery D. Weisman Psychiatry
Consultation Service,
Director, Thomas P. Hackett Center for
Scholarship in Psychosomatic Medicine,
Massachusetts General Hospital;
Boston, MA

FOREWORD

THE BEST INFORMATION SOURCE ABOUT
SERIOUS MENTAL ILLNESS

Facing Serious Mental Illness is for anyone whose life is affected by mental illness. Written by leading psychiatrists and a psychologist, *Facing Serious Mental Illness* combines top-tier medical information and compassionate counsel on the use and tolerability of medications, with a caring and sensible approach to the emotional aspects of living with mental illness and its complications. This book provides easily readable and trustworthy information, which is divided amongst twelve chapters that ask and answer pertinent questions about mental illness and its medical, and psychiatric/psychological components. A glossary of terms provides definitions for medical terminology and jargon; online resources and references are also offered.

PREFACE

Facing Serious Mental Illness is the distillation of knowledge gained after working for several decades with patients (and their family members) who suffer from a serious mental illness (SMI), such as schizophrenia. It employs a user-friendly question-and-answer format to provide practical information on coping with a SMI. Written in an accessible style, this guide is intended for patients (with a SMI) and their family members. Throughout the book, words are italicized to indicate that the terms are defined in a glossary at the end of the book. References are provided for interested readers.

The authors are academic clinicians (psychiatrists [OF, TAS] and a psychologist [CC]) with faculty appointments at Harvard Medical School who have worked on inpatient units, in private practice, and a community mental health center. For 20 years, two of the authors (OF, CC) have provided second-opinion consultations for patients, their family members, and their health care treaters about the nature and treatment of SMI; they have also delivered numerous talks to members of the general public about SMI.

This book attempts to de-mystify SMI and to turn serious psychiatric illness from something frightening and untreatable into something that can be understood and managed. We wrote this book for people with a SMI who want to learn more about managing their illness. However, families dealing with a relative suffering from a SMI will also benefit from reading this book; the more they learn, the better they will be able to support the recovery of their relative while facing an often-long battle with SMI. The book's practical question-and-answer format mirrors questions that our patients with a SMI have asked. While each chapter stands on its own, the book can be read cover-to-cover. It follows the journey from first becoming ill, to seeking help and receiving a diagnosis, to taking charge of their illness, and working with their treatment teams.

We thank our patients (clients) and their families, our trainees, and our colleagues who have shared their stories and whose questions have always guided our work, which attempts to reduce the suffering that stems from living with a SMI.

OF
CC
TAS

WHAT IS SERIOUS MENTAL ILLNESS?

Oliver Freudenreich, MD; Corinne Cather, PhD; and
Theodore A. Stern, MD

CHAPTER

In This Chapter

- Which Conditions Comprise Serious Mental Illness?
- Why Is It Difficult to Live with Serious Mental Illness?
- What Are the Symptoms of Serious Mental Illness?
- What Is Psychosis?
- What Are Schizophrenia-Spectrum Disorders?
- What Is Severe Bipolar Disorder?
- What Is Severe Depression?
- Can Symptoms That Suggest a Psychiatric Illness Be Caused by a Medical or Neurological Problem?
- What Are the Consequences of Serious Mental Illness?
- What Can Complicate the Care of Serious Mental Illness?
- What Role Can the Government Play in Care If You Have Serious Mental Illness?
- How Has Care Changed for People with Serious Mental Illness?

Which Conditions Comprise Serious Mental Illness?

Unfortunately, there is no agreed-upon definition of *serious mental illness* (SMI). Use of older terms such as "serious and persistent mental illness" and "chronic mental illnesses" are now discouraged because they convey a belief that these conditions are untreatable and invariably lead to *institutionalization* in state hospitals. Currently, SMI is characterized by having a psychiatric *diagnosis* with severe psychiatric symptoms, persistent illness, and difficulty functioning in society. This view of SMI implies a need for ongoing psychiatric treatment and societal help; moreover, it encompasses a group of people who have a condition for which a cure is unlikely. Instead, *illness management* is necessary for long periods.

SMI is an umbrella term that captures a diverse array of conditions. However, most of those with SMI have one of three illnesses—*schizophrenia*, bipolar disorder, or chronic depression—which will be the focus of this book. A fourth type, severe personality disorders, will not be covered here because these disorders manifest quite differently than the above-mentioned conditions. People with SMI commonly have one or more *co-morbid* psychiatric conditions, such as *obsessive-compulsive disorder* (OCD), generalized anxiety disorder (GAD), or a substance use disorder (SUD).

To facilitate *epidemiological research* and treatment planning, the federal government operationalized a definition for SMI (Kessler et al, 2003) that included diagnosis, duration, and disability (see Table 1-1).

Table 1-1: Definition of Serious Mental Illness

Primary psychiatric diagnosis (diagnostic criterion)
• Any psychiatric illness (excluding primary substance use disorder and organic disorders)
Prolonged illness duration and treatment needs (duration criterion)
• At least one year
Functional disability (disability criterion)
• GAF score less than 60

Key: GAF = Global Assessment of Functioning
Based on Substance Abuse and Mental Health Services Administration (SAMHSA). In: Kessler RC, Barker PR, Colpe LJ, et al: Screening for serious mental illness in the general population. *Archives of General Psychiatry.* 2003; 60: 184–189.

Why Is It Difficult to Live with Serious Mental Illness?

SMI is common, often distressing, and causes psychological suffering. Unfortunately, having a chronic psychiatric illness can be demoralizing because function in social situations is frequently impaired. In fact, *neuropsychiatric disorders*, including schizophrenia, contribute substantially to *global disease burden*. For example, schizophrenia is one of the top five conditions that contribute to *non-communicable disease* burden.

However, having a SMI creates a problem beyond suffering from the symptoms of the illness: the response of others to those with the illness. In this regard, SMI is unlike any other illness. For example, if you sustain a leg fracture while skiing, you will deal with the medical manifestations of the fracture, but you will probably not be shunned. While you may need to take some time off work, your co-workers will likely be sympathetic, curious, and happy to sign the cast on your leg. However, if you attempt to return to work after a lengthy bout of psychosis, they may think that you will be unable to do your job, become apprehensive, and be uncertain about what might trigger another episode. Some symptoms (such as poor stress tolerance) persist in many people despite treatment and they require accommodations because others have difficulty understanding the experience of residual symptoms. Instead of being understanding and being given a lighter work load, people with depression are sometimes considered to be unmotivated. In other words, people with a SMI must deal with *stigma*, prejudice, and discrimination (Estroff et al, 2004) while managing the symptoms of their illnesses. The ramifications of having a SMI can be summarized in the phrase, "psychosocial toxicities" (see Table 1-2) (Freudenreich, 2020).

Table 1-2: Psychosocial "Toxicities" (Complications) of SMI

• Interrupted schooling and difficulties finishing a degree
• Loss of a job and inability to find a new job
• Legal problems and a criminal record
• Loss of friendships
• Loss of reputation in your community
• Alienation from family members
• Loss of income and the resulting poverty
• Difficulty affording housing
• Social isolation and loneliness

Psychosocial toxicity is a term that emphasizes that psychiatric illnesses are not just brain-based illnesses that can be fixed only by addressing their biology. Instead, it highlights that their societal context is also important. For many patients with SMI, money, housing, and food are key concerns because having a SMI can interfere with reaching life's goals, like getting a good-paying job. Instead, poverty is more prevalent and having housing and securing food is challenging. All too many people with SMI feel lonely and excluded from social activities; both factors are associated with early mortality/premature death.

> ### ⚜ Key Point
>
> SMI can be viewed as a social disease with accrued disability if inadequate treatment is provided. Most types of SMIs are not progressive brain diseases with inevitable downward trajectories.

What Are the Symptoms of Serious Mental Illness?

The core symptoms of SMI depend upon which psychiatric disorder is present. For example, schizophrenia is characterized by prominent psychosis. Mood disorders have symptoms of depression or mania. Symptoms of SMI cross diagnostic boundaries; they are *transdiagnostic* (Fusar-Poli et al, 2019). To make things more complicated, few individuals with SMI develop only psychosis or mood symptoms. Core symptoms of psychiatric diagnoses are often accompanied by non-specific symptoms, like anxiety or insomnia. Some disorders can also have cognitive, behavioral, and emotional correlates. For example, someone with mania might develop rapid thoughts related to having special powers or abilities, become agitated, and report *euphoria*. As noted above, it is not so much the nature of the symptom that determines if someone has a SMI; instead, it is the severity and duration of the symptoms and their effect on function.

What Is Psychosis?

Psychosis is first and foremost a symptom, but it is also a condition or state of mind. In its most narrow definition, psychosis manifests with either *delusions* (fixed false beliefs) or hallucinations (such as hearing, seeing, feeling, tasting, or smelling things that do not exist) (see Table 1-3). Delusions and hallucinations are considered evidence of a person's "break with reality" or impaired reality testing.

Table 1-3: Definition of Psychosis

• Impaired reality testing
• Psychotic symptoms
– Delusions
– Hallucinations
– A formal thought disorder
– Disorganized behavior, including catatonia

Under a broader definition, a *formal thought disorder* and *catatonia* are thought of as *psychotic* symptoms.

Psychosis is also a transdiagnostic symptom that can occur in a wide variety of conditions and with both psychiatric and medical *etiologies* (Freudenreich et al, 2009). For example, about half of people with *delirium* have psychotic symptoms (Meagher et al, 2007). Many drugs, including *cannabis* and lysergic acid diethylamide (LSD), can cause psychosis. Even within psychiatry, a variety of conditions can cause psychosis (for example, delusions or hallucinations also occur in mania or depression). When psychosis complicates mania or depression, a person is thought to have psychotic mania or psychotic depression, respectively.

Psychosis is a technical term with a precise meaning. It should not be used to indicate that somebody has a severe psychiatric condition or one that is not easily understood. Being weird or having peculiar habits or interests does not mean that a person is psychotic. Being violent does not mean that someone is psychotic. For these reasons, a careful clinical interview is necessary to determine if someone is psychotic.

What Are Schizophrenia-Spectrum Disorders?

A spectrum disorder in psychiatry is a mental disorder with a range of severity and manifestations that shares many features. The myriad conditions subsumed under the spectrum disorders are thought to be caused by the same etiology and mechanisms and have similar treatments.

Schizophrenia spectrum disorders are comprised by schizophrenia, schizoaffective disorder, *delusional disorder, schizophreniform disorder*, and sometimes by *schizotypal disorder* (Gaebel, 2012). These disorders have more in common with one another than they have differences, and their diagnostic labels are often neither helpful nor accurate. Although they might differ in disparate symptoms or prominence, their management is very similar. They are likely to be variants (or types) of the same underlying *neurobiological problems*, and the distinction is somewhat academic and rooted in history. Schizoaffective disorder is a good example. At the genetic or biological level, schizoaffective disorder and schizophrenia are indistinguishable, despite slight differences in their symptoms (Paudel et al, 2020). Therefore, it can be better to consider that somebody has a schizophrenia spectrum disorder, which avoids getting bogged down in difficult-to-agree-upon diagnostic details.

Autism spectrum disorder (ASD) is another example of a well-accepted spectrum condition. In this case, the term "spectrum" indicates that people can have symptoms of varying degrees, ranging from very mild to severe.

What Is Severe Bipolar Disorder?

People with bipolar disorder experience discrete mood episodes with a beginning and an end. When untreated, a typical manic episode lasts for several weeks, while a depressive episode lasts for several months before it spontaneously resolves. Between episodes, affected people are in *remission* and they go about their lives. In severe cases, however, the process of recovery from episodes often lasts longer and is incomplete, and people develop many episodes over their lives. In these instances, bipolar disorder becomes a SMI.

What Is Severe Depression?

Like bipolar disorder, people with severe depression either do not recover fully from depressive episodes or have many episodes, which makes recovery between episodes difficult and leads to accrued disability. Severe and chronic depression often renders people unable to work. Severe depression can also be accompanied by psychotic symptoms (thereby qualifying as *psychotic depression*). Such depression is dangerous because it is associated with *suicide*.

Can Symptoms That Suggest a Psychiatric Illness Be Caused by a Medical or Neurological Problem?

"Symptoms in the mind," which is another way of referring to psychiatric symptoms, are not necessarily caused by a psychiatric disorder. There is no one psychiatric symptom that confirms that a psychiatric disorder is present (Freudenreich et al, 2009). Instead, a medical work-up is necessary to exclude medical or neurological diseases as the cause for psychiatric symptoms.

What Are the Consequences of Serious Mental Illness?

In addition to the *psychosocial toxicities* mentioned earlier, having a SMI can reduce your life expectancy. One common cause of death linked with SMI is suicide. Accidents, including some deaths from drug overdoses, are a frequent cause of death. However, so-called "natural causes of death" (such as medical illnesses) are responsible for most of the deaths in those with schizophrenia (Olfson et al, 2015). Over the last two decades, researchers have focused on preventing deaths from *cardiovascular disease* and cancer, which are two leading causes of death. Common causes of death in people with schizophrenia are summarized in Table 1-4.

Table 1-4: Causes of Death in Those with Schizophrenia

Category	Frequency	Conditions
"Natural"	85%	• Cardiovascular diseases • Cancer • Infections
"Unnatural"	15%	• Suicide • Accidents • Drug overdoses

Based on Olfson et al, 2015.

> ### ☆ Key Point
>
> Having a SMI is not just suffering from a psychological affliction; having a SMI comes with the risk of dying prematurely from suicide, accidents, or medical causes. For schizophrenia, the average years of potential life lost per person is estimated to be around 30 years (Olfson et al, 2015).

What Can Complicate the Care of Serious Mental Illness?

Often, the biggest problem for people with SMI and for their families is finding high-quality, comprehensive, and affordable psychiatric care. Unfortunately, services may not be available in your town, and it can be difficult to find a clinic that can manage each of your issues. This is particularly problematic when there is a co-morbid substance use disorder because the mental health care system and the substance use disorder care system are often parallel systems that are incompletely integrated. In addition, insurance companies may limit the type and amount of services or visits that they will reimburse.

Even for families with significant financial resources, organizing psychiatric care for loved ones with SMI can quickly outstrip their available resources.

What Role Can the Government Play in Care If You Have Serious Mental Illness?

Not all people with SMI require a lot of help. Sometimes, medications work well, and treatment only requires an occasional trip to a clinic—as is the case with many other chronic medical conditions. However, at the other end of the spectrum of care, some people need long-term care and life-long help. Providing such a high *level of care* exceeds the means of most families, and a solid public mental health care system is needed to support patients and their families. Without the states' ability to serve as a safety net, people with SMI are at risk for homelessness.

The state is responsible for assuring that its citizens have access to all necessary levels of psychiatric care: outpatient care in the community, short-term hospitalizations, or longer hospitalizations when needed, or a place to go (such as a *group home*) after a hospitalization. A poorly-funded public sector creates gaps in this care continuum that are incompletely addressed by the for-profit private sector.

In many states, services are funded by the state but are no longer provided directly by the state. Instead, private clinics or community organizations (so-called "vendors") are contracted to provide such services. Many states also provide the funding for peer-support services and help with housing and *vocational rehabilitation*.

How Has Care Changed for People with Serious Mental Illness?

How we, as a society, care for people with SMI has changed dramatically over the past 100 years (Freudenreich, 2020b). Gone are the days of "mental institutions" (state hospitals) with thousands of beds that "warehoused" patients. During the period known as "*deinstitutionalization*," the United States drastically reduced the number of its psychiatric beds. Instead, President John F. Kennedy created a network of *community mental health centers* (CMHCs) to help people with SMI live successfully in their communities. What used to be asylum-based psychiatric care has almost completely shifted to community-based care, apart from what are now usually very brief hospitalizations for *acute* care. In fact, in many states, it is now all but impossible to secure psychiatric beds for longer hospitalizations because state hospitals have been closed (Sisti et al, 2015).

It is easy to be critical and to find fault with our current approach, which leaves many patients and their families disillusioned and feeling powerless. However, this is not because of psychiatry's lack of understanding about how to best help those with SMI succeed in society; instead, it is a matter of societal priorities. It costs money to provide psychiatric care, particularly when someone needs lifelong support and works little or not at all.

Underfunded psychiatric care leads to afflicted people falling through the cracks and ending up homeless or in prison. This phenomenon has been called *transinstitutionalization* (Schildbach and Schildbach, 2018).

However, on the positive side, we have learned a lot about how to help people live with SMI. Important conceptual shifts have empowered patients and their families and put patients at the center of care. Patients have a voice and rights, which clearly was not the case in asylums. The role of non-clinical help, like peer support, is another obvious example where progress has been made.

The *coronavirus pandemic* that began in 2019 is likely going to lead to the next revolution in psychiatric care, including care for patients with SMI (Bartels et al, 2020). *Telepsychiatry* is going to play an increasing role, bringing better access to care and more convenience to patients. Patients with SMI are not to be overlooked and left out.

WHEN AND HOW SHOULD I SEEK HELP?

Corinne Cather, PhD; Oliver Freudenreich, MD; and
Theodore A. Stern, MD

In This Chapter

What Can Get in the Way of Seeking Help?

So many things can get in the way of seeking help, and not surprisingly, it often takes years before some people seek out a mental health provider who can help alleviate their suffering from a psychiatric illness. Some of the barriers to seeking help include not having medical insurance or transportation to medical and psychiatric appointments. Also, handling other major life stresses (such as unstable housing, another family member's illness, or one's own personal safety) might be prioritized. Other barriers involve the stigma of mental illness and its treatment. Such stigma includes the fear of being told one has a psychiatric condition, the fear of being labeled as "crazy," being forced to take medication, having concerns about sharing confidential information with a provider, or being told by family and friends that psychiatric help isn't needed. Typically, these illnesses begin in early adulthood when it is natural to want independence. However, as a young person's independence increases and his or her social networks begin to shift, people suffering from these illnesses tend to "fall through the cracks" because their family and close friends aren't there to witness the escalation of symptoms, which means psychiatric care is delayed.

Some people are simply not aware that they need help. They might attribute their struggles to ongoing life stressors or drug use, or they might not recognize that their behavior and internal experiences are linked with mental illness, which is sometimes referred to as "lack of *insight*." Insight lies on a spectrum. Some people realize that they have abnormal experiences but deny that these experiences are caused by a psychiatric illness or that psychiatric treatment may be helpful. In extreme cases, insight can be so impaired that it has been compared to a *neurological deficit* (termed *anosognosia*) (Amador, 2011). Like a person with *Alzheimer's disease* who is unaware of their memory problems (as occurs commonly in later stages of Alzheimer's disease), some people with a *psychotic disorder* do not view themselves as ill. No amount of talking about the problem will change this neurological problem.

Why Isn't It a Good Idea to Delay Seeking Help?

At best, postponing treatment delays complete recovery; at worst, delaying treatment leads to a later and less complete recovery. Delaying recovery can result in more suffering and loss. Delaying treatment of *serious mental illness* (SMI) can lead to lost or damaged relationships (including those with family members), job loss, or school problems. These losses can lead to demoralization and a negative self-concept. Treatment can also be lifesaving. Rates of suicide and violence are significantly elevated among people with SMI who are not receiving psychiatric treatment (Hawton et al, 2005; Alia-Klien et al, 2007).

> 🌿 **Key Point**
>
> Delays in seeking treatment can lead to incomplete recovery; losses in relationships, social roles, and productivity; increased suffering by the person and his or her family; and even death.

What Are Some Pitfalls to Avoid When Looking for Help?

When faced with a problem, most people look for help; however, at times, they look for help in counterproductive ways. The internet is a powerful tool that can provide accurate information about mental health conditions and about how to overcome barriers that interfere with accessing treatment. Well-placed internet searches have the potential to help people obtain timely medical help for their psychiatric conditions. However, one can also access information that can disrupt efforts to get psychiatric care, such as *conspiracy websites* that support and reinforce a person's delusional beliefs or those that promote an exclusive reliance on complementary approaches, as opposed to using standard and effective psychiatric treatments.

Another possible pitfall is looking for help from someone who lacks experience managing SMI. Also, obtaining help from someone who does not have a complete picture of your illness can lead to misdiagnosis, missed *diagnosis*, or minimization of the severity of your mental health condition. Correspondingly, this can lead to substandard or ineffective care, or worse, to no treatment at all. Unfortunately, not all mental health providers are knowledgeable about SMI. For example, one woman with *auditory hallucinations* and *persecutory delusions* told her college counselor that she thought she had *schizophrenia*. The counselor told her that she was "too high functioning to have schizophrenia" and offered *supportive therapy* for depression (which is an ineffective treatment for people with a psychotic disorder).

Although it is natural to conduct research on the internet about the medical difficulties one is suffering, this strategy can lead to inappropriate and inaccurate self-diagnosis. Some people take brief online tests or questionnaires to determine whether they are depressed (for example, using the *Patient Health Questionnaire-9* [PHQ-9]), manic (using the *Altman Self-Rating Mania Scale*), or psychotic. However, these tools might not be valid if people lack sufficient awareness about their conditions, or these tools might only provide a piece of the picture. For example, a person may feel depressed, but this mood may be caused by another condition, such as *post-traumatic stress disorder* (PTSD) and therefore, it might require different treatment than would be used for depression alone. This is one reason why it is important to consult with a clinician who is skilled in considering a variety of psychiatric conditions, with a knowledge base that has been acquired over years of professional training and experience.

> **⚔ Key Point**
>
> Although understandable, excessive internet searching to facilitate self-diagnosis is unlikely to be helpful. Instead, seek out a knowledgeable clinician who can guide you to reputable sources, so you can learn about your condition and its treatment.

Who Should I Go to for Help?

Psychiatrists and *psychiatric nurse practitioners* are the most highly trained mental health professionals regarding making psychiatric diagnoses. Therefore, you should arrange a face-to-face meeting with one of these professionals as soon as possible. However, the path to finding a psychiatrist or psychiatric nurse practitioner can be difficult. The challenge of finding a clinician can be complicated by their low availability in your area and by the scarcity of clinicians who accept payment from your health insurance. Also, many agencies or clinicians have waiting lists and internal policies that require you to see a counselor before seeing a psychiatrist or *nurse practitioner*. Although this additional support can be helpful, this creates frustrating delays for some people, and some people disengage from care before they receive care. The process is made more difficult by being distressed, so you might want to obtain help from someone you trust who can help you sort through the options you have tried, who has returned your calls, and who can provide information about the steps you need to follow to receive care.

> **⚔ Key Point**
>
> Finding a psychiatrist or nurse practitioner can be challenging, and it can be helpful to ask for help and support from someone you trust. Good places to start are your primary care physician (PCP), a college counseling center, and/or an *Employee Assistance Program* (EAP).

You can start by asking your PCP for a recommendation for a psychiatrist or psychiatric nurse practitioner in your area who will accept payment from your health care insurance carrier. If you do not have insurance, you can ask your PCP for the names of clinicians in your local area who provide services for reduced fees or fees on a *sliding scale*. (These services might be offered through your local *community mental health center* [CMHCs] or *community-based health center*). Do not fall into the trap of thinking that a mental health care provider must be expensive to be qualified to help you! Clinicians at community clinics (like a community mental health center) who offer reduced fees are typically well-trained, dedicated, and caring. An additional benefit is that these health care providers understand financial constraints and they can be the most knowledgeable about who is eligible for a variety of services and how to connect with additional supports, such as discounted public transportation, *fuel assistance programs*, *mobile phone subsidies*, food assistance, and housing. State agencies (such as the *Department of Mental Health* [DMH]) can provide you with a list of community mental health centers. If your city has a university or a hospital, you can contact its psychiatry department to get a referral.

If you are employed, you can contact the human resources department at your workplace to learn whether your employer has an Employee Assistance Program (EAP), which can provide you with recommendations. Your employer is mandated by law to keep the information that you share with them confidential. If you are a student, you can start with your school counseling center, which might have psychiatrists on staff to meet with you or to provide recommendations for treatment. Searching online is another option; the *American Psychiatric Association* has a "find a psychiatrist" (http://finder.psychiatry.org/) link that can be helpful. However, you might need to make several calls because these websites do not always show up-to-date information about whether a psychiatrist is taking new patients or accepts your insurance. Another option is a *private pay* or *out-of-pocket* pay option. This might be too expensive as a long-term strategy for most people, but for those who can afford it, it can be a way of getting an evaluation and short-term care quickly. Also, the clinician you contact might be able to connect you with a local psychiatrist for ongoing care.

> ### ✻ Key Point
>
> Expensive treatment is not necessarily better treatment. In fact, many people who pay out-of-pocket for a psychiatrist miss out on other key recovery services.

Just because getting help from a psychiatrist early in this process is advisable, this does not mean that you should rely exclusively on a psychiatrist for help and support. Comprehensive care for SMI is optimized when you have a team of mental health care providers; therefore, you should build this team to promote your optimal recovery. Additionally, you can get help from religious or spiritual communities, holistic practices such as *yoga* or *meditation*, or community groups that have faced mental health challenges. However, it is crucial that you receive a diagnosis first, and psychiatrists or psychiatric nurse practitioners are a good (and necessary) starting point.

How Do I Decide Whether I Need More Intensive Treatment?

For most people with a psychiatric condition, the best starting point is to meet with a psychiatrist or nurse practitioner who provides outpatient care (as opposed to starting with a crisis service or hospital, which is referred to as "inpatient" care). Many people incorrectly believe they will be hospitalized if they tell their health care providers about their psychotic symptoms (hearing voices, feeling paranoid, or having strange thoughts or unusual experiences), or if they share violent or suicidal thoughts. However, the most important factor when considering whether hospitalization is warranted is whether you are currently a danger to yourself or others (or are unable to take of yourself). This can mean that you are making plans to end your life, have recently made a *suicide attempt*, or are threatening to harm or have harmed another person. However, these issues can be more subtle, such as:

- You might be doing things that put yourself at risk of harming yourself or others because of impaired judgment, such as driving at high speeds, walking long distances without shoes, or walking on a highway.

- You might be unable to care for yourself properly. For example, may not be eating because you fear being poisoned.

- Your impaired judgment might interfere with your ability to care for a child or an elder for whom you are responsible.

In these cases, immediate psychiatric care might be required to protect you, your dependents, or society from harm. There may also be treatment options for people in whom concern is high, but not high enough to warrant hospitalization. For example, these services might include a *crisis stabilization unit*, *partial hospital program* (also sometimes called an *intensive outpatient program* [IOP], or *urgent care clinic*).

⚕ Key Point

The experience of psychosis, violent thoughts, or suicidal thoughts per se does not necessarily require that a person should be, or will be, psychiatrically hospitalized. The key factor to consider is current risk to self or others (or inability to care for oneself).

Because it can be difficult for people and families to decide what *level of care* is appropriate, when concern arises about whether you are at risk for harming yourself or others (or have been harming yourself or others), you should seek immediate help through one of three pathways: a *mobile crisis service*, an emergency room (ER), or by calling 9-1-1 in the United States.

Typically, mobile crisis services are 24-hour services provided by mental health clinicians who offer evaluation and support in a person's home. These clinicians will come to your home and talk with you/and or your family and help you decide whether you should have a second evaluation at an ER to determine whether psychiatric hospitalization is recommended. Before conducting their evaluation, crisis teams typically require that you be willing to be evaluated and to remain in your home until the evaluation is complete. You can learn whether you have a mobile crisis service in your area through your health care insurer or by using the *SAMHSA* Treatment Referral Helpline at 1-877-726-4727. It is always a good idea to try to get this information before a crisis has occurred; if there is any concern that things may turn into a crisis, you should investigate whether a mobile crisis unit is available and determine what they can and cannot offer before you reach that point.

Going to your local emergency room is another way to determine whether hospitalization is recommended. As everyone knows, you might need to wait for hours before being seen in an emergency room, so you should be prepared for this and consider having a family member or friend accompany you for support and comfort while you wait. If you think hospitalization will be likely, you should come prepared with a small overnight bag with clothes, toiletries, and things to occupy your time (such as magazines and music). It is also helpful to have a brief written timeline of what you and those close to you have experienced that has led you and/or them to consider hospitalization (see Table 2-1 for an example).

Table 2-1: Sample Timeline of Concern Prepared by an Individual and Family Member

October 15—Called Mom from school, described getting lost using the college shuttle bus system, wound up in an unfamiliar location, and walked home in the dark at 1 a.m.
October 18—Not sleeping well. Parents suggest coming home from school for the weekend. In retrospect, depressed.
October 20—Seems better; goes back to school.
November 15—Parents get call from the dean who has heard from professors and roommates that student is not going to classes or eating meals. Parents go to school, pick up and talk with him about seeing a therapist.
November 16 (The day we went to the ER)—Parents learn from his friend that he is posting things on Facebook that don't make sense about the Illuminati and alternate realities and is talking about suicide. Seems confused and talks about needing to kill himself in order to experience a new reality. Has been researching online how much Tylenol® he needs to take to commit suicide.

When danger is imminent or dangerous behavior has recently occurred, the police should be contacted, by calling 9-1-1 and explaining the situation and that a suspected or known mental health condition is a factor. If you are adamantly opposed to an evaluation—but there is clear evidence of a high risk of dangerous behavior or this behavior has already happened—calling 9-1-1 is a safer option than forcing you to go to an ER. (Tricking someone into going to the ER is never recommended.) Even if you reluctantly go to the ER, you are not necessarily under any obligation to stay. There have been instances when people have hurt themselves by running away or by jumping out of moving cars when forced by family members or friends to go to the ER.

What Is Involved in a Psychiatric Hospitalization?

Psychiatric hospitals have changed over the past few decades. Lengths of stay are shorter—the average length of stay is 1–2 weeks—and people are more connected to the outside world while they are patients because they have cell phones. Patients can have visitors, so you can allow close friends and family to visit and provide support and reassurance. You have access to things that can make the stay more comfortable, such as flowers and snacks. You will be encouraged to participate in groups during the day, to have individual meetings with a therapist and a psychiatrist, and to rest and recover. Some psychiatric hospitals have exercise equipment, such as treadmills, which can be used if you choose. In recent years, psychiatric hospitals have implemented no-smoking policies; smokers are offered smoking-cessation *pharmacotherapy* during the hospital stay.

Even with involuntary psychiatric hospitalization, people who have been hospitalized can often reflect on the hospitalization and agree that it was necessary or helpful. However, you might be very upset about being involuntarily hospitalized and blame family members or health care providers who were involved in the process. This can be challenging for family relationships, and this should be discussed in a family therapy setting because this can clear up misperceptions about what happened, promote greater understanding of each other's perspectives, and draw on the strengths of the family to create a plan to repair these relationships going forward. A necessary hospitalization should not be avoided just because others anticipate difficult discussions after the hospitalization.

How Can I Talk to a Loved One About Getting Help?

It goes without saying that different approaches might be better with different people, so family members need to draw on what they know about their loved ones when deciding which approach to use. Some general guidelines include listening more than talking and expressing empathy for the distressing or difficult aspects of what your loved one is going through.

Listening might require drawing your loved one out to talk about what he or she is feeling and experiencing. You may start by saying something like, "I noticed you seem as though you have been under a lot of stress lately, and I'm here for you if you want to talk about it." Getting people to open up about difficult experiences requires that the listener refrain from responding in ways that shut the person down, so try not to respond judgmentally. For example, don't say, "I told you working and going to school at the same time was a bad idea." Also, be careful not to blame, such as by saying something like, "You are probably causing this by smoking too much pot." Be careful to avoid invalidating, such as by saying, "That's crazy." Avoid creating panic by saying something like, "We need to get you in a psych hospital!"

Instead, family members should try to respond with empathy: "I'm so glad you told me a little bit about what you are dealing with; that sounds tough." "You are really dealing with a lot; I feel for you." You can ask your loved ones about what they have tried thus far and how those approaches have worked. You can ask whether there are other things they have thought of trying but have not tried yet. At this point, your loved ones might even bring up the idea of getting help from a mental health provider. Family members could ask whether there is anything they could do to help with this or any other strategy their loved one is thinking of trying. Your family member's goal should be twofold: first, you want to come to some shared understanding of what your difficulties are, and secondly, your family members should position themselves as allies in helping you face your challenges.

Many people accept help from their loved ones and agree to see a psychiatrist. However, some people are highly resistant to this idea; when this is the case, family members can benefit from getting support from other families who have been in a similar position or by increasing their skills for effective communication with their loved ones. The *National Alliance for Mental Illness* (NAMI)'s Family-to-Family program is an excellent option for getting support from other families. Family members might also want to learn more about the *LEAP method* (see Table 2-2).

Table 2-2: The LEAP Method

Listen	Use reflective listening skills to demonstrate understanding.
	• Example (depression): "I hear you. You have no energy or hope for things getting better in the future, and sometimes, it's so bad that you wonder if it's even worth going on."
	• Example (paranoia): "It is so hard for you when you worry that your family might be actually trying to harm you by putting poison in your food."
	• Example (mania): "You are feeling a lot of excitement but also a lot of pressure to make things happen right now, and that can be stressful."
Empathize	Get in the person's shoes and respond with compassion for what he or she is going through.
	• Example: "You are going through such a tough time, I really get that."
Agree	Find areas of agreement around how to conceptualize the patient's struggle.
	• Example: "It sounds like the worst part of this for you is that you feel isolated and disconnected from other people."
Partner	Become an ally in the service of helping the person get help.
	• Example: "You mentioned that one thing you are feeling overwhelmed with is getting your phone fixed. Is there any way I could help with this?"

Adapted from: Amador X: *I'm Not Sick and I Don't Need Help.* New York: Vida Press; 2011.

What Are Some Obstacles to Seeking Help?

You should avoid nagging or badgering the person with a SMI about seeking mental health services, taking medication, or tackling other issues. Try to avoid putting him or her "under a microscope" and analyzing everything he or she does and says through the lens of dealing with a mental health issue. For example, family members should consider whether they would have had the same reaction to their loved one not shaving or cleaning up after him/herself before becoming aware of the mental health issues. Alternatively, it is also important that family members not abandon expectations around behavior or to "walk on eggshells" around their loved one. Although more challenging in the context of mental health issues, family members should stay focused on the relationship, do enjoyable activities together, and consciously carve out time together that is not dominated by issues related to mental health or treatment. (See Table 2-3 for tips for helping a loved one as recommended by Mueser and Glynn, 1999.)

Table 2-3: Tips for Helping a Loved One with Mental Health Issues

- Keep expectations minimal, but don't let them all go.
- Encourage, but do not nag. Choose your battles.
- Help your relative keep a routine that is as close to normal as possible.
- Don't argue with your relative over worrisome thoughts.
- Continue to do enjoyable activities together.
- Don't argue about the "reality" or a diagnosis.

It is often counterproductive to offer advice to someone who is ambivalent or clearly opposed to treatment. The problem with jumping right into a problem-solving mode is that it may make the person feel as though you are not listening and as though he or she is losing control over what happens to him or her. Your goal is to keep the lines of communication open when it comes to how he or she is feeling about possible solutions. At some point, you (or another family member or close friend) might want to float the idea of having an evaluation with a psychiatrist to sort through what is going on and help him or her move forward.

What Are a Family Member's Options If Their Loved One Refuses Help?

Family members whose loved ones refuse help are in a very difficult situation. Some families have shared heartbreaking stories about how it has not been possible to get their loved ones to treatment, despite their best efforts. Sometimes, as a result of the illness, the relationship becomes strained or even completely estranged. In a minority of cases, when people show an inability to perceive the realities of their own condition (anosognosia), no amount of talking or flexibility will prevent the person from rejecting help. Thankfully, in most cases, family members can make some headway with their loved ones who are not fully onboard with treatment through compromise, a change of approach to enhance *motivation* for treatment, systems change, or acceptance.

When a loved one rejects psychiatric treatment, find out whether he or she has other ideas about what would help them feel better. Maybe a compromise can be reached in which this alternative is pursued for a certain amount of time, and if objective and subjective indices do not improve, an agreement can be reached to see what psychiatry may have to offer.

Another possibility is to change the approach used. Some families use rewards to encourage patients to adhere to treatment. For example, an agreement can be made such that parents' financial support for college is contingent on not using substances. The patient could be required to share toxicology test results—tests that are administered at random or on a predetermined schedule. Alternatively, access to the family car or financial assistance could be contingent upon proven adherence to prescribed medication. This approach is referred to as "*contingency management*," and for it to work, there must be follow-through on the positive or negative consequences. Sometimes, family members undermine these approaches by making empty threats and then not following through on them, such as by saying, "Unless you take your medication, you can't live here." Working with a family therapist can be helpful in planning for how to construct realistic contingencies and implement these approaches in such a way that they have a chance of being effective.

Another way of changing the approach is to shake up the current way in which treatment recommendations are being made, such as involving a new family member in these discussions. Sometimes, people are more open to encouragement to pursue treatment from a family friend, cousin, or sibling than they are to their parents. Another option is to consider an alternative living environment, such as a staff-supported residential placement (see Chapter 7 for a description of these settings and how to access them) or living with another family member, so that treatment recommendations come from a source other than the nuclear family.

Acceptance is perhaps the most difficult-to-master skill (but the most powerful) for people and family members affected by mental illness. Suffering is a part of life. None of us knows what form it will take in our own lives, but it is unavoidable. Mental illness is an example of that suffering. We can do what we can to lessen it, and usually, we are successful. However, there are limits to what we can achieve, even under the best circumstances. Patients and caregivers who are open to that reality find that their quality of life is improved. For most people, a full acceptance of illness and treatment is both illusory and unnecessary. Most patients with SMI have enough awareness about their predicament that they accept treatment but also enough (perhaps protective) denial of illness that allows them to be hopeful about their future.

For some people with a SMI and no insight, assisted treatments may be necessary. Delaying or ignoring the need for involuntary psychiatric help in such difficult cases deprives people of the chance to get better or worse, and can lead to premature death or other tragic outcomes, such as homicide. Some states have involuntary treatment options beyond the psychiatric emergency (such as *outpatient commitment* and *contingent discharge*). In some cases, you and or your family may be advised to consider the option of putting a legal *guardianship* in place. It is very important to work with an attorney with experience in this area and to select the type of guardianship (e.g., full, limited, temporary) which puts protection in place for health or safety, while allowing you to retain as much independence as possible. Judicial oversight of involuntary measures is *de rigeur* and a safeguard against inappropriate use of state power.

WHAT MAKES DIAGNOSING SERIOUS MENTAL ILLNESS IMPORTANT?

Oliver Freudenreich, MD; Corinne Cather, PhD; and
Theodore A. Stern, MD

CHAPTER

In This Chapter

- Why Is Making a Diagnosis Important?

- What Looks Like Serious Mental Illness but Isn't?

- Do I Need to Be Evaluated by a Psychiatrist?

- How Is the Diagnosis of Serious Mental Illness Made?

- What Kinds of Questions Will I Be Asked by Mental Health and Medical Professionals?

- What Kind of Tests Might I Undergo?

- Do I Need a Brain Scan?

- Should I Get Psychological Testing?

- Why Can Establishing the Diagnosis of Serious Mental Illness Be Challenging?

- Can Mental Health Conditions Co-Exist?

- What Questions Should I Ask Practitioners Who Are Evaluating Me?

- How Am I Likely to Feel When I Am Receiving a Diagnosis of Serious Mental Illness?

Why Is Making a Diagnosis Important?

An adage, attributed to the German poet Goethe "The Gods have put *diagnosis* before treatment," is consistent with a key concept in medicine: It is generally better to treat something that is named because it is understood, such as when the causes of a condition, and not just its *signs* and *symptoms* are known. Signs and symptoms alone, without being placed in the context of how, when, and why they arise, are non-specific and do not guide best practices. Knowledge of diseases, on the other hand, leads to specific interventions that are based on the causes *(etiology)* of the disease and their biological mechanisms *(pathophysiology)*. For example, take headache. It is essential to know whether a headache flows from a serious neurological condition, such as a *brain tumor*, as opposed to a *migraine*. Making the correct diagnosis is important so that the proper treatment can be selected and implemented.

However, even without knowledge of their etiology and pathophysiology, psychiatric disorders can be treated specifically and effectively. Having a diagnosis also helps with planning the next steps in a person's life. Knowing if symptoms will resolve completely with treatment or persist despite treatment guides therapeutic adjustments and accommodations.

For many people, receiving a psychiatric diagnosis removes doubts and perplexity (such as, "What is going on? Why do I feel like this?") and turns a disease into something manageable. Practically speaking, a diagnosis is often needed to access care and facilitate payments by *third-party payers*.

> ### ❊ Key Point
>
> Treatment is predicated on the diagnosis: the diagnosis (the name of the condition) guides treatment (using interventions that are specific for the diagnosis) and determines the prognosis (the short- and long-term outcome, with or without treatment).

What Looks Like Serious Mental Illness but Isn't?

Psychiatric symptoms (or "symptoms in the mind," as a seminal book on *psychopathology* calls them [Oyebode, 2018]) are non-specific. Sometimes, feeling depressed is temporary and a clear response to an outside stressor. While distressing, such symptoms are not indicative of a *serious mental illness* (SMI).

Many medical mimics of psychiatric symptoms need to be considered (Freudenreich, 2012). Feeling sad and depressed may suggest "psychiatric" depression or it could stem from a variety of medical conditions, such as thyroid dysfunction. Figure 3-1 depicts how psychotic symptoms can arise in a variety of psychiatric conditions *(primary psychosis)* and can also be caused by a medical condition, substance abuse, medications, or toxins *(secondary psychosis)* (Freudenreich et al, 2009). Table 3-1 lists non-psychiatric *(organic)* conditions that can cause psychosis.

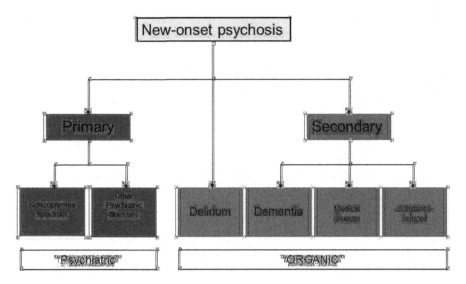

Figure 3-1: Schematic for categorizing conditions that cause new-onset psychosis.

Table 3-1: Organic Causes of Psychosis (Broad Categories with Common Examples)

Medical Causes
• Genetic disorders
• Endocrine disease (such as hypoglycemia, hyperthyroidism, or hypothyroidism)
• Metabolic diseases
• Autoimmune diseases (such as systemic lupus erythematosus [SLE])
• *Narcolepsy*
• Neurologic conditions
– Stroke
– Seizures
– Demyelinating diseases (such as multiple sclerosis [MS])
– Autoimmune inflammatory brain diseases (such as NMDA receptor encephalitis)
– Basal ganglia diseases (such as Huntington's disease, Wilson's disease, Parkinson's disease)
– Traumatic brain injury (TBI)
– Dementias (such as Alzheimer's disease [AD] or Lewy Body Dementia [LBD])
– Brain tumors

continued

Medical Causes (continued)
• Vitamin deficiencies
• Infections (such as herpes simplex encephalitis, neurosyphilis, human immunodeficiency virus [HIV], or Lyme disease)

• Substances of abuse
  − Alcohol and sedatives (during intoxication and *withdrawal*)
  − *Cannabis* and cannabinoids
  − Simulants (such as cocaine or amphetamines)
  − Lysergic acid diethylamide (LSD) and other hallucinogens (such as psilocybin)
  − Phencyclidine (PCP) and ketamine

• Medications and toxins
  − Medications (such as glucocorticoids, isoniazid [INH], mefloquine, digoxin, or levodopa)
  − Toxins (such as carbon monoxide, heavy metals, or organophosphates)

The old term for secondary causes of psychiatric symptoms is "organic" which indicates that it is based in biology, and it is not merely a symptom in the mind. However, the term "organic" has fallen out of favor because all symptoms in the mind are brain-based. In a similar fashion, psychosis can be attributable to a combination of factors (such as *delirium*, which is often multi-factorial) and each of them must be systematically considered.

Do I Need to Be Evaluated by a Psychiatrist?

Psychiatrists are medical doctors (MDs) who go through extensive medical training focused on the diagnosis and the treatment of mental disorders. Psychiatrists are trained to think about the *differential diagnosis* of symptoms (meaning a list of other conditions that could be responsible for symptoms), specifically if psychiatric symptoms can be explained by medical or toxic-metabolic causes. This is one of the most important goals of a diagnostic interview: deciding whether a medical or neurological cause is responsible for psychiatric symptoms or whether the problem is a primary psychiatric condition.

In addition, psychiatrists are trained to develop a comprehensive treatment plan that often includes the use of psychiatric medications. While psychiatric providers (such as *nurse practitioners* [NP]) can write prescriptions, many other psychiatric providers, such as *psychologists* and *therapists*, typically cannot prescribe medications. It makes sense to seek a diagnostic evaluation from a psychiatrist, especially if medications might be helpful.

How Is the Diagnosis of Serious Mental Illness Made?

The most important tasks for making a diagnosis involve conducting a *clinical interview* ("gathering a history") and performing a physical examination. Laboratory testing is then ordered to confirm or refute initial diagnostic impressions derived from the history and the exam.

Psychiatrists make diagnoses in the same way that non-psychiatric physicians do: by obtaining the history of symptoms and conducting the psychiatric equivalent of a physical exam, which is called the *mental status examination* (MSE) (see below). A psychiatrist then synthesizes all the information obtained to create a working diagnosis. Not uncommonly, it can take more than one meeting or consultation visit to formulate a diagnosis, particularly if the history is complicated. In most cases, long-term follow-up will refine the diagnosis, although atypical or complicated cases often lead to delays in making a definitive diagnosis.

᠉ Key Point

It is often helpful to obtain the perspective of someone else, like a family member, so-called sources of *collateral information*, to clarify timelines and to add observations.

Most diagnoses can be made by listening to and interpreting the history. Preparing for a consultation visit is helpful to psychiatrists, so that they will have access to critical information, even before your appointment. However, at times, less is more. It is a rare practitioner who reviews 100 pages of clinic notes from years of therapy. Table 3-2 provides a list of helpful documents to gather or prepare before having a psychiatric consultation.

Table 3-2: Items to Prepare for Initial Evaluation/Psychiatric Consultation

- Time-line of symptoms
- Summary of psychiatric treatments (such as maximum dose, duration, and reason for discontinuation)
- Hospital discharge summaries (patients need to request these from the medical records department of each hospital)
- Test results (of brain imaging and laboratory tests)
- Results of neurocognitive testing
- Letters from other consultation visits
- Current medication list, with medication doses and their schedule

What Kinds of Questions Will I Be Asked by Mental Health and Medical Professionals?

A comprehensive exam will focus on the symptoms you are experiencing and on how they affect your wellbeing and functioning. The mental status exam examines your thoughts, feelings, and behaviors; it contains both subjective information and objective data. Its main components are listed in Table 3-3.

Table 3-3: Key Components of the Mental Status Examination

• Appearance, attitude, and behavior (including eye contact and psychomotor abnormalities)
• Affect and mood
• Speech and thought process
• Perception and thought content (delusions, overvalued ideas, obsessions; thoughts of suicide [suicidal ideation; SI], and homicidal ideation [HI])
• Sensorium and cognition (awareness; orientation; attention; memory; and intelligence)
• *Insight* and judgment

The psychiatrist will ask you about when your symptoms started and how they evolved. In addition, gathering the history will clarify how your symptoms changed in relation to medical conditions, to drug use (if present), and to social circumstances (for example, a death in the family or life stressors [such as moving homes or beginning college]). You will also be asked about your upbringing, traumatic experiences, and your family's history of mental illness. Engaging in a comprehensive interview should not feel like you are completing a checklist, but instead feel more like a conversation about your life (such as how you grew up, how you did in school or at work, what your family and social life was like, and how your psychiatric symptoms interfered with those domains).

What Kind of Tests Might I Undergo?

Sometimes it is difficult to tell whether psychiatric symptoms stem from a psychiatric disorder or from a medical problem. There are no so-called *pathognomonic* signs that provide you with complete certainty. Some laboratory tests are ordered to exclude common and likely organic causes. Similarly, the extent of testing is guided by the clinical interview. Some routine tests (often called *baseline labs*) are done to determine if your major organs (such as your kidney, liver, and heart) are working normally, and to prepare for safe prescribing of medications. More specific testing, like an *electroencephalogram* (EEG), would only be ordered if there is suspicion of a *seizure disorder*. Table 3-4 lists laboratory tests that a psychiatrist might consider when treating a person with their first-episode of psychosis. For other psychiatric disorders, the list would look different.

Table 3-4: Initial Work-Up for a Person with a First-Episode Psychosis

Laboratory Tests
• Broad screens:
– Complete blood count
– Electrolytes including calcium
– Renal function tests (blood urea nitrogen [BUN]/creatinine)
– Liver function tests
– Erythrocyte sedimentation rate (ESR)
– Antinuclear antibodies (ANA)
– Glucose
– Urinalysis
– Urine drug screen
• Tests for specific abnormalities:
– Thyroid stimulating hormone (TSH)
– Vitamin B_{12} and folate
– HIV screening[b]
– FTA-Abs for syphilis
– Ceruloplasmin[c]
Neuroimaging
– MRI to rule-out demyelinating disease, a brain tumor, or stroke[d]
• Ancillary tests, as clinically indicated
– Electroencephalogram (EEG)
– Chest X-ray (CXR), lumbar puncture, blood cultures, arterial blood gases (in infections)
– Autoantibodies (in cerebrospinal fluid [CSF])
– Karyotype (early-onset schizophrenia)

continued

Laboratory Tests (continued)
• Ancillary tests, as clinically indicated *(continued)*
– Serum cortisol
– Medication drug levels
– Toxin search

Key:
[a]This list is not exhaustive but represents one possible initial work-up. Other tests should be considered if the history and the clinical picture suggest that they might be useful diagnostically, in the context of epidemiology and immune status.
[b]Recommended as part of routine care for any patients.
[c]Extremely low yield, many false positive results.
[d]Controversial as low yield.
Adapted from Freudenreich et al, 2007.

Even if a test is positive, it still requires clinical judgment to determine if the result explains the symptom. An example of such a test result is a positive *urine drug screen* for cannabis in a person with psychosis. This finding could be coincidental and not explain the person's psychosis (for example, the psychosis would be present even without cannabis in the bloodstream).

> ### ☆ Key Point
>
> A *"shotgun approach"* of ordering a panel of tests is an ineffective strategy for medical practice. Tests are best ordered when they reflect a clear clinical suspicion of a disease and that test can then confirm or refute the hypothesis. Otherwise, tests that are ordered "just to be sure" can generate false-positive test results (abnormal lab value in the absence of disease) that can complicate management because those results will need to be repeated and or other tests will be ordered.

Do I Need a Brain Scan?

Patients often ask if brain imaging will help to make a diagnosis of a SMI. At present, obtaining brain imaging (like a *magnetic resonance imaging* [MRI] *scan*, a *computed tomography* [CT] *scan*, or a *positron emission tomography* [PET] *scan*) cannot be used to diagnosis a psychiatric illness. However, these tests can rule-out other illnesses. For older patients in whom *dementia* or a *stroke* might account for psychiatric symptoms, brain imaging is part of a standard workup.

The situation is different for healthy, young adults who present with a first-episode of *psychosis* or a first-episode of *mania*. Brain imaging is unlikely to show anything other than non-specific and clinically unimportant abnormalities, with the same frequency that is present in *healthy controls* (Lubman et al, 2002). For example, most guidelines for *schizophrenia* do not recommend ordering brain scans routinely in the evaluation of those with first-psychosis. However, knowing that a brain scan is normal (i.e., that a serious condition, like a brain tumor, is not present) can be both reassuring and helpful to patients and families, thereby facilitating a focus on the management of the psychiatric disease.

In the future, more sophisticated *functional imaging* that combines several imaging modalities might be available for use in clinical care. Currently, those tests are only completed for research purposes (not for diagnostic purposes).

Should I Get Psychological Testing?

A variety of psychological tests are available, including *aptitude tests, intelligence tests,* or *personality tests*; some psychological personality tests are called *projective tests*. Projective tests can support clinical impressions. However, they cannot be used alone to make a clinical diagnosis; these tests should not be used to make a diagnosis in the absence of supporting clinical information.

Instead, your psychiatrist might recommend *neurocognitive testing* to delineate cognitive strengths and weaknesses. Neurocognitive testing can examine, among other things, processing speed, attention/vigilance, *working memory*, verbal and visual learning, reasoning and problem-solving, and *social cognition*. Testing should focus on memory, attention, and executive function. The results are helpful most often for treatment planning rather than for diagnostic purposes. These tests should be ordered after the *acute* phase of the illness so that the person can engage optimally in the tasks.

Why Can Establishing the Diagnosis of Serious Mental Illness Be Challenging?

In medicine, physicians usually have laboratory tests to confirm an initial diagnostic impression. For example, if a *myocardial infarction* (MI) *(heart attack)* is suspected, a *cardiologist* will order blood tests and imaging tests to confirm the diagnosis. In psychiatry, there are no such confirmatory laboratory tests. Tests are only used to exclude medical conditions that can mimic a psychiatric disorder.

Other challenges are created by the fact that disorders must "declare themselves." Schizophrenia, for example, has a long phase of non-specific symptoms before the onset of psychosis; this is called the *prodrome*. Until psychosis develops, schizophrenia cannot be diagnosed. An often-underappreciated problem is that many people have received a variety of treatments, including medications that can that can treat (suppress) symptoms. For example, non-specific and mild paranoia and irritability can be effectively treated with an antipsychotic, but it can prevent a diagnosis from being made because insufficient symptoms can be elicited to make a diagnosis. Cooperation creates another challenge. Because making a psychiatric diagnosis hinges, to some degree, on people describing their inner experiences, not all people can do this well—or they refuse to do so. The results of diagnostic interviews can be challenging as they require the interviewer to interpret when people have a very different explanation of their inner experiences than do those close to them. For example, people who have *delusions of persecution* will be contradicted by family members who confirm that the beliefs are out-of-character and not grounded in a realistic fear (for example, of persecution). It can also be difficult to interview someone who is denying the existence of symptoms, perhaps because of (understandable) fears of the consequences of admitting them to a psychiatrist or another care provider. Collateral information from friends and families can be of critical importance in these cases; however, such collateral sources might not be available.

In some instances, it is impossible to know if symptoms are solely from substance use, or if psychiatric symptoms would disappear if substance use were to stop. Periods of abstinence from substances (such as during an extended hospitalization) can be helpful in clarifying the diagnosis.

✤ Key Point

A psychiatric diagnosis is a clinical diagnosis that is based on current psychiatric symptoms and how these symptoms have evolved over time. There is no substitute for a clinical interview that reviews the time course of symptoms, and there is no laboratory test that can confirm a clinical diagnosis of schizophrenia, bipolar disorder, or depression.

Can Mental Health Conditions Co-Exist?

Schizophrenia, for example, involves more than just psychosis. Other illness dimensions include *motor symptoms, cognitive symptoms, negative symptoms,* or *affective symptoms.* These illness dimensions are part and parcel of schizophrenia and do not necessarily require separate diagnoses. However, if severe enough, giving separate diagnoses (such as schizophrenia and recurrent depression) points toward additional treatment targets. The combination of *bipolar disorder* and *attention deficit disorder* (ADD) is another example. Most people with a SMI are diagnosed with more than one psychiatric disorder. Such *co-morbidity* is often a reflection of diagnostic preference and does not necessarily mean that a person has two or more psychiatric disorders.

Most clinicians try to identify conditions to facilitate optimal treatment and to not overlook a treatable condition. Someone with schizophrenia might have *social anxiety* that can be treated with anti-anxiety treatment, as opposed to simply dismissing social uneasiness as "being part of schizophrenia."

To complicate matters, people might also receive different diagnoses at different times as diagnoses are only based on symptoms that may change over the course of a person's life.

SMI and *substance use disorders* (SUDs) are commonly co-morbid; the term *dual diagnosis* is often used when this occurs. Cigarette smoking could also be considered a common co-morbid condition.

> ### ⚘ Key Point
>
> So-called co-morbidity between psychiatric disorders and substance use disorders is the norm and not the exception. Co-morbid conditions are important (as they can be specifically treated) and can interact: The presence of one can make the other more difficult to treat. For example, the presence of cannabis use makes it more difficult to treat schizophrenia.

What Questions Should I Ask Practitioners Who Are Evaluating Me?

Patients and families usually have many questions after finding out that their loved one has a SMI. Education about the optimal management of illnesses like schizophrenia or bipolar disorder is not a one-time event but an ongoing process. Over time, some answers become clearer while other questions arise.

Some families have already suspected that a problem exists and they come prepared with specific questions, while others need to hear more about basic things. Table 3-5 provides examples of questions that patients and families have for evaluating clinicians.

Table 3-5: Questions to Ask During a Psychiatric Evaluation

Patients
• How sure are you (the psychiatrist) about the diagnosis?
• What other diagnoses did you consider?
• Are there any tests that will help determine the diagnosis?
• What are initial treatment options?
• Do I need to take medications?
• Can use of medications be delayed?

continued

Patients (continued)
• What treatments, other than medications, offer the best hope for recovery?
• What can I do to support my recovery?
• How can I decide if I need to go to the hospital?
• Where can I learn more about my condition?
• When should I return to work or school?
Families
• What can we do to best support our loved one?
• How can I be legally involved in the care of my son or daughter?
• When should we (the family) ask for urgent help?
• How can we help even if no help is requested?
• How should we respond when he or she talks about things that we believe are not based "in reality?"
• Should we apply for help from the state?
• Am I able to keep my son/daughter on our family's health insurance plan even if he or she is over 26?

How Am I Likely to Feel When I Am Receiving a Diagnosis of Serious Mental Illness?

People have varying reactions upon learning that they may have a SMI, particularly if the diagnosis is a *schizophrenia spectrum disorder*. In medicine, receiving a diagnosis for unexplained symptoms is often met with by relief: The not-knowing and uncertainty have finally been given a name. Now that the "enemy" is known, action can be taken.

However, psychiatric diagnoses usually require more extensive explanations. For some, the diagnosis comes as a shock because the person never thought that he or she would develop a psychiatric illness. Others have suspected that they have a SMI and they feel relieved. Some families have already had experience with mental illnesses and receive the diagnostic information calmly. Diagnostic uncertainty intrinsic to psychiatric disorders often complicates how information about a diagnosis is processed by patients and their families.

Many people and their family members go through a range of emotions that can be compared to *grief*. The framework for stages of grief developed by Kübler-Ross can be applied to SMI as well (Kübler-Ross, 1969). An initial period of shock and denial ("It was just stress") might be followed by anger ("Why me?") and bargaining ("It does not affect me that badly"), depression, and ultimately, some period of acceptance. These stages might not follow in sequence, they might be mixed, and there might never be "closure."

Not everyone accepts the diagnosis of mental illness, particularly an illness like schizo-phrenia. Much effort is spent on the quest for another, more "medical" diagnosis that can ultimately hinder progress and increase the duration of untreated psychosis (if antipsy-chotic administration is delayed).

WHAT ARE THE GOALS OF PSYCHIATRIC TREATMENT?

Oliver Freudenreich, MD; Corinne Cather, PhD; and
Theodore A. Stern, MD

In This Chapter

- What Is the Purpose of Psychiatric Treatment?
- When Should I Focus on Medical Health?
- What Is Remission?
- How Important Is Relapse Prevention?
- Should I Aim for Symptom Reduction, Improved Function, or Enhanced Quality of Life?
- What Is Quality of Life?
- Should Loneliness Be a Concern of Treatment?
- What Types of Tools Might Be of Help to Me?
- What Is a Treatment Plan?
- When Should I Take Medications?
- Should I Begin a Talking Therapy?
- When Should I Start Psychiatric Rehabilitation?
- Who Should Determine My Treatment Goals?

What Is the Purpose of Psychiatric Treatment?

Psychiatric treatment saves lives and can prevent serious negative, long-term, life consequences. It can prevent suicide or death from an accidental drug overdose or from accidents that occur during an episode of *psychosis*. It can prevent violence against family members, legal difficulties, and coercive treatment, which adversely affects future involvement in treatment. Delays in treatment and treatment involving an inappropriate *level of care* (for example, a person should be an *inpatient* but is an *outpatient*) can lead to untoward complications.

Most people hope that psychiatric treatment will return their lives to the level they achieved before they became ill. Such a *restitutio ad integrum* (Latin for "restoration of full health") or cure is often not realistic, except for *acute* conditions (such as an infection or a broken leg). For *chronic* conditions, recovery goals often need to be defined more conservatively, and patients and families should be encouraged to celebrate partial victories, such as fewer *symptoms*, returning part-time to school or work, and working toward a good *quality of life* (QOL) despite residual symptoms and other challenges.

A helpful distinction in treatment goals differentiates among symptoms, quality of life, and function. Figure 4-1 depicts how these variables were related in a group of young people with *schizophrenia* (Lambert et al, 2008). After one year of treatment, roughly 60% of patients achieved symptomatic *remission*, 57% reported a good QOL, and 45% returned to function. However, only about 30% reported minimal symptoms, good QOL, *and* good function, which is arguably the type of remission that people with schizophrenia and their families are seeking.

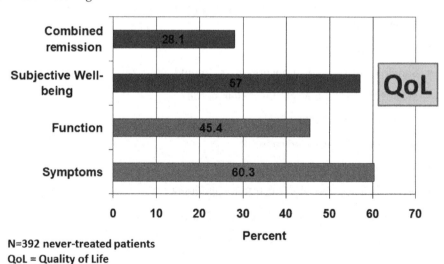

N=392 never-treated patients
QoL = Quality of Life

Figure 4-1: Symptoms, function, and quality of life as treatment targets (Lambert et al, 2008).

When Should I Focus on Medical Health?

Preventing medical *morbidity* and *mortality* from psychiatric treatment is a key concern for psychiatrists (Goff et al, 2005). *Iatrogenesis* is a term used when a problem stems from the medical intervention itself, such as a medication-induced side effect. For example, many psychiatric medicines cause weight gain that needs to be managed to reduce the side effect burden from treatment. However, medical and psychological health are intertwined. There is no mental health without physical health! The reverse is true as well. People who are psychiatrically ill often struggle to manage their overall physical health.

> ### 🌿 Key Point
>
> *Mens sana in corpora sano* is an old Roman adage from Roman poet Juvenal's Satire X (line 356): A healthy mind in a healthy body. Physical and psychological health need to be addressed simultaneously. One does not exist without the other.

What Is Remission?

Remission is a medical term used to describe an improvement in symptoms or even a temporary disappearance of symptoms. It does not imply a cure. One needs to be specific: Remission with regards to what? All symptoms? Just psychosis? A useful way to think about *sustained symptomatic remission* is that it is the basis for *rehabilitation* (with its focus on function) and a good quality of life (Andreasen et al, 2005).

How Important Is Relapse Prevention?

For chronic illnesses (like schizophrenia or *bipolar disorder*) that often have episodes of illness, preventing future *psychotic, manic,* or *depressive episodes* is a high-priority treatment goal. Sustained symptomatic remission is the basis for making progress with regard to school, work and friendships. Put differently, frequent *relapses* make getting back on your feet within society nearly impossible. Each relapse can undo months or years of hard work and progress.

Should I Aim for Symptom Reduction, Improved Function, or Enhanced Quality of Life?

Those goals are not mutually exclusive! Well-constructed treatment plans take into account all three goals when deciding on the best course of action. Often, a good starting point is symptom control because symptoms are typically what bring people to a clinic or hospital for help. Without symptom reduction, for example, severe anxiety or depression, it can be very difficult to function.

However, you should not expect these goals to develop in sequence. QOL is considered when medications (with few side effects) are chosen to reduce symptoms. Also, the connection between symptoms and function is not tightly bound. Simply waiting for symptom resolution can be a poor strategy because some symptoms might never resolve completely. The task is often to figure out what you can do despite having symptoms. While most people think that having fewer symptoms is linked to functioning better, the salutary effects of work are well established: Work also reduces symptoms. *Salutogenesis* is a medical approach to health and well-being that examines how factors (like work) promote health, in contrast to having a narrow focus on the use of medications for disease management (Mittelmark et al, 2017).

Ultimately, those with the disorder need to decide what matters most to them. Sometimes, having more symptoms is tolerable if the side-effect burden is low and the drug is safer when a lower dose of a medication is used.

What Is Quality of Life?

A person's QOL can be viewed as a summary of how they are doing. "Subjective wellbeing" is another term for QOL. QOL for most people means their view about how things are going. In the realm of health care, pain and depression are the two most important subjective factors that lead to poor QOL. However, we also know that environmental factors (such as having money, having a job, being in school, having housing, having a good social network) affect stress levels, and they influence QOL (Fleury et al, 2013). Four domains of QOL can be identified (see Table 4-1) (World Health Organization). Increasingly, *patient-centered care* uses QOL as a crucial outcome measure even when the primary outcome is something like survival rates, such as in a cancer trial.

Table 4-1: Four Domains of Quality of Life

Domain	Facets
Physical health	Pain, sleep, mobility, and energy
Psychological	Self-esteem, anxiety and depression, body image, and spiritual life
Social relationships	Personal relationships, social support, and sex life
Environment	Financial resources, safety, housing, access to health care, opportunities for leisure and learning

Based on The World Health Organization Quality of Life (WHOQOL) scale, https://www.who.int/mental_health/publications/whoqol/en/.

✵ Key Point

QOL is a treatment target in its own right, because it is not necessarily tied to symptoms and function (Valiente et al, 2019).

Should Loneliness Be a Concern of Treatment?

More and more people in the United States live alone and are lonely, particularly as they age, as long-term friends, acquaintances, and loved ones die (Murthy, 2020). Increasingly, *loneliness* is recognized as an important source of psychological suffering in societies that value individualism. This "loneliness epidemic" exacts not only a psychological price but also seems to be a risk factor that contributes to premature death; it is comparable to smoking 15 cigarettes per day (HRSA, https://www.hrsa.gov/enews/past-issues/2019/january-17/loneliness-epidemic). Loneliness literally kills people because it is, biologically speaking, a stressful state (Holt-Lunstad et al, 2015). Grief is an example of typically temporary and situational loneliness. People can die from a lonely heart after losing someone close to them.

Loneliness is a subjective experience that involves being isolated from others and from society. Researchers differentiate between intimate (emotional), relational (social), and collective (societal) loneliness regarding the connections among loved ones, networks of friends, and society at large, respectively. *Anomie* is a sociological term to describe the disconnectedness of a social group from the norms and values of society, and it is a key factor in the "deaths of despair" because of suicide or drug use that has gripped a bevy of countries.

The quality—not just the quantity—of relationships matters. You can be lonely in a crowd. Companionship is what is needed; you do not need to have the most friends on Facebook. Not all relationships are desirable. For example, some people manage their fear of loneliness by accepting unhealthy connections, for example, with those who use illicit drugs. Moreover, we don't all need to have the same number of friends to feel supported. Most of us are quite happy having only a few good friends. If you are unsure about the number of good friends you have, ask yourself the question: "Would this person pick me up from the airport or train station at night or help me move my stuff?" However, cultural differences also exist, depending on cultural expectations and norms that shape our experience of loneliness.

Solitude is not to be confused with loneliness: It is a state of being by oneself but without accompanying loneliness. Achieving solitude is a sign of health and not something that needs to be "fixed." Being physically isolated, however, can be a risk factor for loneliness. Just looking at the number of social contacts a person has made in a week is often used as a measure of loneliness. For many people, the onset of a serious psychiatric illness is followed by the loss of relationships. A painful alienation from friends, co-workers, and family members can occur because many people turn away when an illness does not improve and isolation can become chronic (Eglit et al, 2018). If this occurs, many people end up lonely, with a socially impoverished life. While developing new relationships and social connections can be difficult, developing them might become an important goal of treatment. People with *serious mental illness* (SMI) might need help when loneliness begets more loneliness. In a vicious cycle, people increasingly stop seeking social connections for fear of not fitting in (due to *stigma*). Like QOL, loneliness is one of the seemingly "softer" treatment targets that can make all the difference in a patient's life, if it is recognized and addressed successfully. Social connectedness is an evolutionary biological need that requires social prescribing in the form of social community activities and resources. *Peer support* is an example of a widely available program to address, among other things, social isolation.

> ### ❦ Key Point
>
> Loneliness is a signal that a biological need for connectedness is not being met. Being part of a community and a neighborhood that literally and figuratively cares about you is an antidote to loneliness and its adverse effects on emotional wellbeing and physical health. Lonely people might need quite a bit of help to reconnect because they have unlearned how to connect with others; moreover, some people might be fearful of rejection or exploitation.

What Types of Tools Might Be of Help to Me?

Your treatment team has a large tool box to help you with your psychiatric condition. Three important tools are medications, *psychological therapies*, and *psychosocial rehabilitation*. Each of these is discussed individually in the chapters that follow.

Referring to these three interventions as "tools" conveys crucial connotations: They are only tools, not ends in, and of, themselves. Just "being on a medicine" is not a treatment goal unless the treatment with medications also achieves clear objectives, such as better symptom control or relapse *prevention*. Similarly, "being in therapy" cannot be a goal, unless the engagement in therapy serves some larger purpose. Moreover, there is more than one approach to addressing psychiatric problems. Community engagement is another important tool that is not included in a narrow definition of psychiatric treatment.

What Is a Treatment Plan?

In a thoughtful treatment plan, your treatment goals should be delineated, along with the tools to achieve those goals. Unfortunately, all too often, a treatment plan is a bureaucratic document that is filled out as a formality with little meaningful input from the patient and his or her family. Those mandated treatment plans are relics from a time when patients were warehoused in state institutions offering little treatment (Dragatsi et al, 2019). Instead, *treatment planning* (a process of engagement to create living a document that reflects the negotiation between all parties involved) is needed, to achieve the best possible outcomes and recovery, and to achieve outcomes that are realistic yet hopeful.

Treatment-goals are phase-specific. After their first episode of psychosis, young people often have different goals than those of older persons with long illnesses. For example, a younger person's interest in work might differ. However, what is shared between patients of all ages are their hopes for the best possible QOL, with few treatment side effects, and with meaningful things to do.

When Should I Take Medications?

Your doctor will typically recommend taking a psychiatric medication for two different reasons: The medication will likely manage your acute symptoms during an acute episode, and it will prevent relapse after the episode has been treated. You should understand the difference between these two scenarios. In the first case, medications are used to reduce distressing symptoms, such as psychosis, depression, or mania. In the second case, the main symptom (for example, psychosis) is successfully treated and the symptoms are gone (for example, symptomatic remission is achieved). Medication is also used to prevent the return of symptoms (with the goal being sustained symptomatic remission). In this case, the medicine is sometimes falsely believed to no longer be needed. In this case, stopping medicine can result in relapse.

You should also be realistic about what medications can do and what they cannot do. To state the obvious, medications cannot give you your life back. If you dropped out of school or lost your job, you will need help returning to school or finding a new job. Some forms of rehabilitation might help you achieve those goals. Medicines, nevertheless, will often allow you to achieve such goals. As noted earlier, sustained symptomatic remission will often help alleviate symptoms that are interfering with such goals.

It cannot be overemphasized that medications are often a critical part of treating SMI; however, they are only one tool. They do not create jobs or help you make friends. The analogy with back pain might help. If you have acute back pain, a pain-relieving medication might be needed to reduce your pain before *physical therapy* (PT) intended to strengthen your back. Both are needed for the best outcomes! Without psychiatric medications to reduce your psychological pain, it might not be possible to apply for jobs or make friends.

Should I Begin a Talking Therapy?

Many people find *psychotherapy* to be one of the most helpful aspects of psychiatric care. However, therapy alone is not considered the best treatment for chronic illnesses, such as bipolar disorder, schizophrenia, or *schizoaffective disorder*, and therapy is often more effective when used in combination with medication. Therapy is often the place in which people develop the skills needed to achieve their personal goals. For example, a psychiatrist might be very aware of your loneliness and talk with you about deserving friends and about some community resources where you might be able to find peer support. Your therapist might extend this discussion to include the qualities you value in a friend, specific social contacts you might want to reconnect with, and role-play how you can hone your skills needed to initiate conversation with others. Once a person has both a *psychiatrist* and a *therapist*, he or she has a team. Not only can more be accomplished with a team—both the therapist and the psychiatrist can help the person optimize his or her use and benefit of both treatment modalities.

When Should I Start Psychiatric Rehabilitation?

There is an old saying in psychiatry that says, "rehabilitation starts with the hospital admission: as early as possible and not only when somebody has no symptoms anymore." Rehabilitation is pursued in parallel with treatment of psychiatric symptoms; it is not sequential. Sometimes, people will say things like, "I'll restart school once I no longer hear the voices." However, because these are relapsing conditions and because many people will not achieve full symptomatic remission, a person would do well to learn how to pursue rehabilitation goals despite ongoing symptoms. Otherwise, delays can contribute to these skills getting "rusty" and blocking the resumption of these life activities.

Who Should Determine My Treatment Goals?

In modern medicine and psychiatry, patients decide on their treatment goals. The term patient-centered care (or also *person-centered care*) captures this sentiment. As the name implies, patient-centered care puts the patient in the center of psychiatric interventions. Patients drive their care and are active participants in their care; they are not the passive recipients of care. Ideally, patients have people they trust to help them decide what course of action to take. These may be family members or friends. Deciding on treatment goals is a collaborative effort between patients and treatment providers. Deciding on treatment goals is also a negotiation, particularly when goals seem unrealistic or simply impossible.

⚕ Key Point

Doctors and Family Members: stop asking, "What is the matter with the patient?" Instead, ask, "What matters to them?"

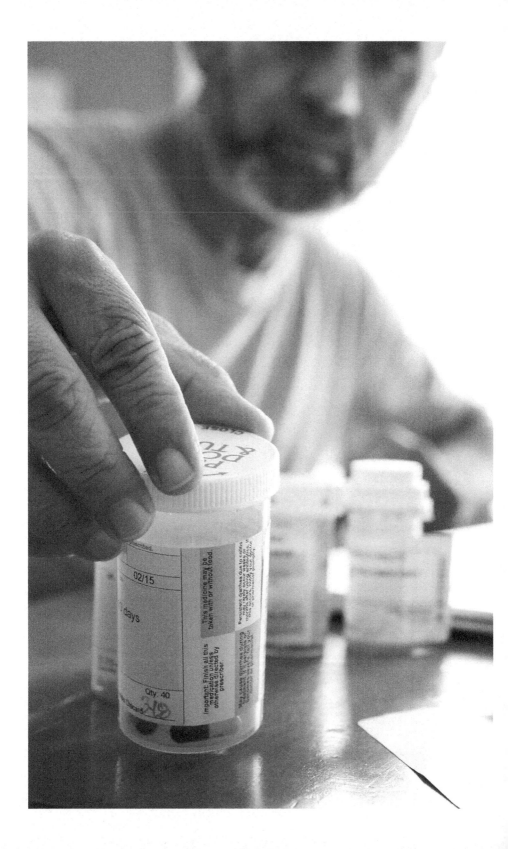

WHAT TYPES OF PSYCHIATRIC MEDICATIONS SHOULD I CONSIDER?

Oliver Freudenreich, MD; Corinne Cather, PhD; and
Theodore A. Stern, MD

CHAPTER 5

In This Chapter

- What Are Psychotropics?

- What Classes of Medications Can Treat Symptoms of Serious Mental Illness?

- What Types of Antipsychotics Are There?

- What Are the Benefits of Taking Psychotropics?

- How Do I Pick the Best Psychotropic for Me?

- Which Side Effects Can Result from Use of Psychiatric Medications?

- What Are Typical Side Effects of Antipsychotics?

- What Are Metabolic Side Effects of Antipsychotics?

- What Are Extrapyramidal Symptoms?

- What Is Tardive Dyskinesia?

- What Are Typical Side Effects for Mood Stabilizers?

- What Are the Side Effects of Lithium?

- Can Side Effects of Medications Used for Serious Mental Illness Be Prevented and Treated?

- What Blood Tests Do I Need When I Take Psychiatric Medications?

- How Long Will I Need to Take Medications?

- What Can I Do to Remember to Take My Medication?

- When Should I Consider a Long-Acting Injectable Antipsychotic?

What Are Psychotropics?

Psychotropics are psychiatric medications that act on your mind—as the Greek name for mind, "psyche" implies. They are used to treat non-specific psychiatric symptoms, including impairments in thinking, disturbances in feelings, and problematic behaviors. Psychotropics are used to treat distinctive psychiatric disorders like *schizophrenia, bipolar disorder*, and *depression.*

Psychotropics are a diverse group of medications that can be grouped into four categories based upon their indications for use. *Antipsychotics* are for *psychosis; antidepressants* are for depression; *mood stabilizers* are for bipolar disorder; and *anxiolytics* are for *anxiety.* However, the names of these medication classes are problematic because their clinical effects are not limited to a single target. For example, antipsychotics work for mood disorders and reduce anxiety, and mood stabilizers are often used for schizophrenia. And surprisingly, antidepressants do not work well for *bipolar depression*——despite their name. Note that there are no "anti-schizophrenia medicines" because schizophrenia involves more than just psychosis.

Some medications were re-purposed from common *neurologic* applications. For example, many mood stabilizers such as *valproate* are anti-epileptic drugs (AEDs) that are used for the treatment of *seizures* and *epilepsy.*

❋ Key Point

You cannot determine what psychiatric condition is being treated by looking at a person's medication list. The Food and Drug Administration (FDA)-approved usage list merely shows that a drug company sought and received FDA-approval for a particular use as a result of conducting clinical trials. For this use, the medication is safe and effective, as determined by FDA regulations. Most medications have many clinical uses that are not reflected by their FDA-approved uses.

The official worldwide "real" name for medications is called their *international non-proprietary name* (INN). The INN often refers to the chemical structure of the medications, which is probably the least helpful way to learn about them unless you are a *chemist* or go to medical school. Still, *benzodiazepine* anxiolytics *("benzos")* are a well-known group of medications that refer to an agent's chemical structure and that has made its way into popular culture. "*Decanoate*" is another example where a chemical property is used as a short-hand to refer to a medication; in this case, a *first-generation antipsychotic* (FGA) is linked to a decanoate *fatty acid* tail to make it longer -lasting. Older antidepressants, such as *tricyclic antidepressants* (TCAs) or "*tricyclics*," have a three-ring molecular structure.

Drug companies use *brand names* that are usually easier to remember and pronounce. *Generics* often use the INN, although the two terms are not always identical.

Ideally, medications are grouped based on their *mechanism of action* (MOA). This is common practice in medicine. For example, *beta-blockers* or *angiotensin-converting enzyme* (ACE) *inhibitors* that are used to treat *hypertension* signify their MOA. For some psychotropics, a MOA is presumed based on their *receptor profile* or *target protein*. For example, all currently-used antipsychotics block the *dopamine-2 receptor* in the brain; therefore, they are *dopamine antagonists. Selective serotonin re-uptake inhibitor* (SSRI) antidepressants interact with the *serotonin transporter* in the brain and block serotonin uptake into *cells*. Unfortunately, the MOA for many psychiatric medications is not yet understood. *Lithium*, a salt that was found to have mood-altering effects many decades ago, affects numerous cell processes. For most psychotropics, it is likely that their MOA involves more than one cellular process, and it cannot be reduced to an action on one receptor or one target protein.

While efforts are underway to standardize the *nomenclature* for psychotropics in the form of a *"Neuroscience-based Nomenclature"* (NbN) that uses the pharmacological profile of a psychotropic, a wide variety of terms remain in use (Zohar and Kasper, 2016).

What Classes of Medications Can Treat Symptoms of Serious Mental Illness?

The most important classes of psychiatric medications that treat people with a *serious mental illness* (SMI) are antipsychotics, mood stabilizers, antidepressants, and anxiolytics. However, many other medications are used to target symptoms, including *stimulants* (for low energy/fatigue) or *hypnotics* (for sleep).

Mood stabilizers are medications that are used primarily to treat the highs (*hypomania* and mania) and lows (depression, *dysphoria*) of bipolar disorder *(manic-depressive illness)*. Lithium is the *gold standard* mood stabilizer, with broad effectiveness against all phases of bipolar disorder. Many other mood stabilizers are AEDs. The best established mood stabilizers are valproate *(valproic acid)*, *lamotrigine*, and *carbamazepine*. However, AEDs are not as broadly effective as is lithium, and not all AEDs have mood-stabilizing properties. For example, *gabapentin* is ineffective against bipolar disorder. In addition, antipsychotics also have mood-stabilizing properties.

Antidepressants effectively treat a wider array of conditions than their name implies. In addition to depression, they treat a range of *anxiety disorders, obsessive-compulsive disorder* (OCD), and trauma-related disorders, such as *post-traumatic stress disorder* (PTSD).

⅍ Key Point

Despite their name, antidepressants are not a good medication choice if you have bipolar depression. At best, they are ineffective. At worst, they destabilize the illness or induce mania. The mainstay of treatment for bipolar disorder are mood stabilizers, among which lithium is the most effective.

Modern anxiolytics (or *sedative-hypnotics*) largely fall in the benzodiazepine class of medicines. They differ from one another in their *half-life* and *metabolism*. In addition to managing anxiety, they are also often prescribed (and marketed) for treatment of impaired sleep. The main concern with use of benzodiazepines is *addiction*, so judicious use of them is required. However, they are very effective for the management of *acute* anxiety, psychological distress, or short-term, stress-induced *insomnia*. On the other hand, their long-term use is generally not recommended (although it is commonly practiced). The exception is when anxiolytics are used for specific conditions, such as *catatonia*.

What Types of Antipsychotics Are There?

For historical reasons, antipsychotics are often grouped into *first-generation antipsychotics* (FGAs), *second-generation antipsychotics* (SGAs), and *third-generation antipsychotics* (TGAs). The FGAs go back to the 1950s and were called "typical" *neuroleptics* because they cause "*neurolepsis*" in animal models (literally making an animal stiff). The prototype of a FGA is the first marketed antipsychotic, *chlorpromazine (Thorazine™)*, which is named after the hammer-wielding god of Germanic mythology. FGAs are further classified by their potency (i.e., the number of milligrams needed to achieve the desired clinical effect), which predicts some side effects. SGAs were initially called "atypical antipsychotics" because they did not cause neurolepsis, at least not at commonly prescribed doses. The first atypical antipsychotic was *clozapine*. Subsequently, atypical antipsychotics became known as SGAs, starting with *risperidone* in 1993. The most recently developed group, TGAs, do not fully antagonize the dopamine-2 receptor; this makes their receptor-binding profile quite distinct from FGAs and SGAs. The overall receptor profiles for antipsychotics are complex and their MOA is not well understood. Table 5-1 provides a classification that is based, in part, on their receptor profiles.

Table 5-1: Antipsychotic Clinical Groups

Class	Dopamine Receptor	Examples
FGAs	Dopamine$_2$ antagonists High-potency Mid-potency Low-potency	*Haloperidol*, fluphenazine Loxapine, perphenazine Chlorpromazine
SGAs	Dopamine$_2$/5-HT$_2$ antagonists	Asenapine, clozapine, iloperidone, lumateperone, lurasidone, *olanzapine*, paliperidone, quetiapine, risperidone, ziprasidone
TGAs	Partial dopamine$_2$ antagonists	Aripiprazole, brexpiprazole, cariprazine

Key:
FGA = first-generation antipsychotic
SGA = second-generation antipsychotic
TGA = third generation antipsychotic

> ### ⚕ Key Point
>
> Antipsychotics are a diverse group of medications. While textbooks often group them into bins (first-, second-, third-generation antipsychotics), it is better to view each antipsychotic in its own right with its own unique receptor profile. Other than clozapine, the efficacy of antipsychotics is comparable, although individual responses might differ (Huhn, 2019). Where they differ from one another is in the side effects they produce: Antipsychotics are markedly different in their side effects and tolerability.

What Are the Benefits of Taking Psychotropics?

For acute complaints, medications are used to treat individual *symptoms* or to target a cluster of symptoms (a *syndrome*). For example, an anti-manic mood stabilizer is used to treat the syndrome of mania; the assumption here is that as the syndrome gets better, all symptoms improve. A syndrome-based approach, if possible, is usually better because it "kills two birds with one stone" and it avoids *polypharmacy*.

> ### ⚕ Key Point
>
> Psychotropics can be given acutely to treat individual symptoms (like insomnia) or to treat an acute episode of illness (targeting a syndrome), or they can be given chronically for the *prevention* of illness episodes.

Even if medications do not immediately treat *core symptoms* like psychosis, medications are quite effective in reducing the suffering that comes from having psychiatric symptoms. For example, if you are manic, psychotic, or depressed, you might also experience severe sleep problems that can be helped with medications. Those effects are often readily apparent to you and to others. People who are psychotic are often afraid; this feeling is helped by use of an antipsychotic even though *paranoia* itself does not improve immediately. People with depression can be very anxious and agitated, feelings and behaviors that are helped by antidepressants, even if the corresponding mood does not immediately brighten. Over time, all the symptoms that come with an episode resolve. It is important to wait long enough because it takes time for acute episodes of illness to resolve.

A good analogy for understanding how psychiatric medications are used comes from the management of back pain. If you have new-onset and severe back pain, you might need an acute intervention, such as rest, and a strong pain-relief medication to ease your discomfort because physical therapy is not possible when your pain is overwhelming. Similarly, when you are acutely psychotic, hospitalization and treatment with an *antipsychotic* medication provides much-needed relieve from mental suffering and it ultimately allows you to participate in therapy and in psychosocial rehabilitation once the acute symptoms improve. Just like those with back pain can learn how to live with, or despite, back pain as long as the symptoms are not overwhelming, psychiatric symptoms need not disappear to work on getting better.

Some medications, such as benzodiazepines that are prescribed to improve sleep, are only used in the short-term and then they can be discontinued.

How Do I Pick the Best Psychotropic for Me?

Modern psychiatry is *patient-centered*: The voice of patients matters. Your voice is particularly important when deciding when to try a psychiatric medication and which medication to use. Just like with any medication, your doctor should involve you in the decision about which medication would be best for you. Working with your treatment team to arrive at a decision is called *shared decision making* (SDM).

However, not all decisions are equally important and several factors affect shared decision-making (Hamann and Heres, 2014). In many instances, your doctor will not have a strong opinion about which medication to use (or even whether to use one at all), and the choice is based solely on your preference *(preference-sensitive decision)*. For example, you may choose a medicine based on the side effects that would be acceptable (or unacceptable) to you. For some people, gaining a few pounds is not a big deal; for others, weight gain (of any amount) is a deal breaker.

> ### 🌿 Key Point
>
> The differences between the efficacy of psychotropics are often not the driving forces for choosing which medication to try. For example, antipsychotics have comparable efficacy (with the exception of clozapine). However, they differ significantly in their side effect profiles, which become a main point of discussion.

Frequently, doctors agree that a certain medication is the treatment of choice, which means that your doctor might favor a particular medication and try very hard to get you to agree with the recommendation (best-choice decision). However, in some situations (for example, a life-or-death situation), the clinic or hospital is legally and morally required to proceed with treatment regardless of a person's opinion—at least initially.

> ### 🌿 Key Point
>
> Before beginning any medication, your doctor should talk with you about its risks, benefits, and alternatives—including no treatment. Knowing these three things is the basis for *informed consent*.

Shared decision-making does not mean that your doctor passively outlines the options and then sits back and lets you make a choice, like choosing food from a menu. One option might clearly be the best, with the second- or third-line options being less-than-ideal. In all jurisdictions, an involuntary hospitalization requires a significant element of risk to the person or the community. The tolerance of risk varies greatly and can lead to different recommendations.

Which Side Effects Can Result from Use of Psychiatric Medications?

Considering the vast array of potential side effects is a crucial component of deciding whether to take a medication. The decision to use a medication should involve a great deal of thought. Its use should have a clear goal—and all interventions should be initiated after a thoughtful appraisal. "Just trying something" is never a good strategy. Even medications that are usually safe can have serious and *idiosyncratic* side effects, such as *allergic reactions*.

Doctors often think about how much to tell you and they attempt to strike a balance between providing too little information and overwhelming you with information that is neither relevant nor important. Your doctor should discuss with you rare but dangerous side effects as well as common and expected side effects because these are what most people should pay attention to when starting a medication.

Discussions about medications are ongoing; they are not a one-time event. Moreover, not all side effects need to be discussed at the beginning of treatment. You should read the *package insert*, look up medicines on the internet, and then discuss what you found with your doctor to put the information into a meaningful context.

Most medications have short-term side effects and long-term side effects. Early side effects often disappear once your body has adjusted to the medication. The biggest mistake many people make is to stop a medicine after one or two doses. Instead, it is prudent to discuss problems with your doctor as they arise and develop a plan of action that might include staying the course. Abandoning a potentially helpful medicine too early, before it has had time to work, is problematic because this strategy might remove this medicine from future consideration (because some people will consider this a failed trial). Long-term side effects, such as weight gain, need to be managed as long as you are taking the medicine.

What Are Typical Side Effects of Antipsychotics?

The list of potential side effects of antipsychotics is lengthy (almost any *organ system* can be affected) and differs significantly among antipsychotics.

Antipsychotics used to be called "*major tranquilizers*" because some degree of sedation is common, particularly at the beginning of treatment. Taking the medicine at night usually resolves this issue by turning sedation into a beneficial side effect by helping you to get a better night's sleep.

Many important side effects are related to the *dopamine blockade* of antipsychotics. Motor side effects (known as *extrapyramidal symptoms* [EPS]) and elevation of *prolactin* levels are common problems that are associated with the use of FGAs and some, but not all, of the newer antipsychotics because they tightly bind to and block dopamine. Elevation of prolactin levels is associated with unwanted sexual side effects, *galactorrhea*, and in the long run, *osteoporosis*. If those problems develop, switching to a *prolactin-sparing antipsychotic* such as *quetiapine* or *aripiprazole* solves the problem.

Antipsychotics also have long-term side effects (such as weight gain, metabolic problems, and *tardive dyskinesia* [TD]) that emerge only after weeks or months of treatment and that require monitoring and attention.

What Are Metabolic Side Effects of Antipsychotics?

Unfortunately, almost all antipsychotics cause some degree of weight gain. Since most people try to lose weight and not to gain weight, weight gain can be problematic. From a medical perspective, weight *per se* is not the issue. Instead, the hazards of weight gain are its long-term medical consequences, such as diabetes and *lipid* abnormalities. There are clear differences between antipsychotics with regard to the likelihood of causing weight gain (see Table 5-2).

Table 5-2: Antipsychotics—Metabolic Risk

High	Clozapine, olanzapine
Medium	Risperidone, paliperidone, quetiapine
Low	Lurasidone, ziprasidone, aripiprazole, brexpiprazole, cariprazine, lumateperone, haloperidol, fluphenazine

In addition, the risks associated with different types of weight gain also differ. Some antipsychotics cause metabolic derangements beyond what you would expect from weight gain alone. For example, weight gain with aripiprazole is metabolically not as dramatic as the same degree of weight gain with olanzapine. The most problematic type of weight gain can be invisible because it develops mostly in your gut. If advanced, it can lead to an apple-shaped abdomen that is best assessed by looking at somebody's *waist circumference* and not merely quantifying the "number" of pounds gained. In medicine, the *body mass index* (BMI) is preferred over a person's absolute weight in pounds because it is a better measure of a person's body fat. The BMI is used to classify whether a person's weight is normal or if a person has overweight or obesity.

Your metabolic status is often summarized as the "*metabolic syndrome*," which is a constellation of findings as summarized in Table 5-3. Its importance lies in its association with heart disease. For all practical purposes, each of the factors in the syndrome should be addressed individually. For example, your doctor would treat hypertension and *diabetes*, and manage excess weight.

The behavioral management of weight while taking an antipsychotic is important. Your doctor might suggest that you take a medication, such as *topiramate*, to reduce weight, and to prevent diabetes by taking *metformin*.

Table 5-3: Components of the Metabolic Syndrome

Three or more of:

- Abdominal obesity measured by waist circumference (men greater than 102 cm [40 inches]; women greater than 88 cm [35 inches])
- High fatty acids (greater than or equal to 150 mg/dL)
- Low high-density lipoprotein (HDL) "good" cholesterol (men less than 40 mg/dL; women less than 50 mg/dL)
- Elevated blood pressure (greater than 130/85 mmHg or any treatment for hypertension)
- Elevated fasting glucose (greater than 110 mg/dL)

Based on National Cholesterol Education Program (NCEP) ATP III Guidelines.

What Are Extrapyramidal Symptoms?

The antipsychotics' actions on the *basal ganglia* cause a variety of motor side effects (that is, affecting muscle tone and movement) called *extrapyramidal symptoms* (EPS) (Freudenreich and Flaherty, 2018). These side effects include *akathisia*, an *acute dystonic reaction*, *Parkinsonism*, and *tardive dyskinesia* (TD). Those side effects are more likely to occur with the use of FGAs. However, even next-generation antipsychotics can create motor side effects, particularly if you are sensitive to them. With the exception of TD, motor side effects generally resolve once your antipsychotics have been discontinued.

Akathisia is a side effect that can arise after taking your first dose. It is an unpleasant feeling in the lower extremities that makes it hard to sit still; you might feel compelled to walk about. An acute dystonic reaction is also an early side effect that consists of painful and often frightening muscle contractions (cramps). It often affects your neck muscles, leading to involuntarily movement of your head to the side *(torticollis)* or your eyes moving upwards *(oculogyric crisis)*.

Parkinsonism resembles *Parkinson's disease* and consists of the cardinal triad of motor symptoms: resting *tremor*, rigidity (being stiff), and bradykinesia (moving slow). As the name implies, the typical tremor occurs only at rest. It usually becomes apparent after several weeks of treatment. Like most EPS, it is more likely to develop with the use of FGAs.

Many psychotropics, including mood stabilizers, cause tremor. Lithium often causes a fine tremor, even when used at *therapeutic doses*. However, tremor can also be a sign of *lithium toxicity*.

What Is Tardive Dyskinesia?

The most problematic long-term side from taking dopamine-2 blockers (antipsychotics) is tardive dyskinesia (TD) (Correll et al, 2018). TD causes abnormal, involuntary movements that are described as "choreo-athetoid," which are like the movements seen in *Huntington's disease*. Such movements are twisting, writhing, irregular, and fast (but not as fast as *tics*), and often affect the tongue, mouth, jaw, face, and fingers. If detected early, the antipsychotic can be stopped, which often leads to the resolution of this potentially irreversible side effect.

Thankfully, TD is rarely severe. However, even when it is mild, it can interfere with social interactions, because even subtle movements of the face will identify a person as "different." It is encouraging that effective and well-tolerated FDA-approved treatments with *VMAT-2 inhibitors (deutetrabenazine, valbenazine)* became available for the treatment of TD (Solmi et al, 2018) in 2017, although their high costs can be prohibitive.

Prevention is much preferred over the need for treatment. For some conditions, the risk of TD might not outweigh the benefits of antipsychotics. A conservative approach might include not using antipsychotics for conditions other than schizophrenia, bipolar disorder, and serious depression. If an antipsychotic is needed for those disorders, the lowest effective dose should be used for the shortest period possible. Not all situations require *maintenance treatment*. For schizophrenia, where maintenance treatment is needed, there might be little choice. However, even newer antipsychotics are linked with some risk of TD (Carbon et al, 2017). The standard of care is to screen on a regular basis for the onset of abnormal movements as a harbinger of early TD. The *Abnormal Involuntary Movement Scale* (AIMS) screening test is recommended for documenting the presence (and absence!) of abnormal motor movements during *antipsychotic treatment*.

What Are Typical Side Effects for Mood Stabilizers?

The *antiepileptic drugs* (AEDs) with mood-stabilizing effects often have side effects: sedation, *nystagmus*, and tremor. Older AEDs such as carbamazepine and valproate require blood monitoring and can be challenging to use. Next generation AEDs are better tolerated. With some mood stabilizers, it is not uncommon to develop a rash.

What Are the Side Effects of Lithium?

Lithium has a narrow *therapeutic index*, which means that the difference between a therapeutic dose and a toxic dose is quite small. This can be managed with blood level monitoring (see below). Lithium toxicity is can be dangerous and it typically presents with a coarse tremor, diarrhea, and confusion. Common lithium-induced side effects that arise at usual doses include tremor and frequent urination. The main long-term concerns for lithium are *chronic kidney disease* (CKD) and *hypothyroidism*, both of which require blood monitoring.

Can Side Effects of Medications Used for Serious Mental Illness Be Prevented and Treated?

Often, early-onset side effects disappear after taking a few doses if you continue taking the medication. It is important that you not stop the medicine on your own; instead, you should discuss the problem with your doctor. For example, taking a medicine with food (if there is nausea) or switching from morning to night dosing (if there is sedation) can help you adjust to the medicine during the early phase of treatment. Do not stop medications suddenly unless the problem is severe. Your doctor should provide you with a list of symptoms that require immediate action.

For many side effects, a variety of interventions is possible, such as adjusting the dose, adding an antidote for a side-effect, or switching to a different medication. For some side effects, active management is needed as long as you are taking the medication. Monitoring and managing weight gain with a combination of *behavioral interventions* and medications are important efforts. Preventing diabetes associated with antipsychotic-related weight gain by adding metformin is an example of a medical intervention that can be considered if you have to take one of the metabolically higher-risk antipsychotics (Gerken et al, 2016).

What Blood Tests Do I Need When I Take Psychiatric Medications?

Most psychiatric medications, such as anxiolytics or *selective serotonin re-uptake inhibitors* (SSRIs), are safe and do not require regular blood monitoring. For other medications, regular monitoring of blood levels is necessary to use the medications safely. For example, lithium can cause *renal* and *thyroid* dysfunction that needs to be monitored closely. For antipsychotics, blood work should be obtained at least once a year to monitor for metabolic side effects, such as elevated levels of cholesterol.

Many medications (antipsychotics and many antiepileptic mood stabilizers) have an optimal or therapeutic blood level range. For those medications, *therapeutic drug monitoring* (TDM) is helpful. In the case of lithium, TDM is mandatory because it has the afore-mentioned narrow therapeutic index. TDM for antipsychotics is generally most helpful to determine if a dose is sufficient or excessively high (Schoretsanitis et al, 2020). TDM for clozapine is well established, and clozapine dosing should be guided by TDM results.

Doctors often do blood work and an *electrocardiogram* (ECG) before prescribing any psychiatric medications, even if the medications are very safe, to ensure that there is no problem. For antipsychotics in particular, establishing baseline values for metabolic parameters, such as weight and markers for diabetes and lipid abnormalities, should be obtained and repeated at regular intervals throughout treatment. In uncomplicated cases, repeating blood work once a year is sufficient. Table 5-4 summarizes the baseline assessments that are typically obtained before starting an antipsychotic.

Table 5-4: Typical Antipsychotic Baseline Assessment

• Weight and height to calculate the BMI
• Waist circumference*
• Blood pressure*
• Blood work: fasting blood sugar* and HbA1c, fasting lipid panel*
• Electrocardiogram (ECG)
• Note absence or presence of abnormal movements (using the AIMS)

BMI = Body mass index
*Components of the metabolic syndrome

How Long Will I Need to Take Medications?

In the hospital, people are often treated with a variety of medications to control symptoms quickly and to make people less distressed. For example, benzodiazepines are "prescribed as needed" (*pro re nata* [prn]). This does not mean that the regimen started during an acute inpatient stay must be maintained as an outpatient. If side effects emerge, your doctor will usually simplify your medication list or change your treatment to a better-tolerated regimen over time.

Once a year, your doctor might consider "deprescribing," which means reviewing all your medications to see if they are all still needed and stopping those for which the benefit no longer outweighs the risks (or the original purpose of starting them got lost over time). Too often, medications that are not working are continued ("maybe they help a little"), while new medications are continually added.

⅍ Key Point

It is as important to know when and how to stop medications as it is to know which medication to start. Often, a time-limited trial with a clear goal and duration in mind should be agreed upon. Identifying a target symptom that is measured (rated) on a simple scale from 1 to 5 is critical to avoid the accrual of medications of unclear benefit.

What Can I Do to Remember to Take My Medication?

Most psychiatric medications need to be taken every day for them to work best. Even forgetting antipsychotics every few days can lead to more symptoms. Treatment *adherence*, specifically adherence to medications, is a critical goal of medication management (Goff et al, 2011).

A common mistake is trying to remember taking medications without any help. This does not work well, particularly for medications that need to be taken for more than a few days. You need to create a system that works for you: Do not rely on your memory. Instead, taking medications should be incorporated into your routine. Taking a medicine every night after brushing your teeth is one such routine because taking the pill becomes a habit that you do not have to think about, such as brushing your teeth. Some people like to use pill boxes or other forms of reminders. If you find yourself frequently forgetting to take medications, despite your best efforts, enlist the help of others.

When Should I Consider a Long-Acting Injectable Antipsychotic?

Long-acting injectable (LAI) medications are an excellent first-line treatment to manage chronic conditions—making it convenient so that you do not need to remember to take your medications (Freudenreich and Cather, 2012). For schizophrenia, LAIs are highly effective in preventing subsequent psychotic episodes (Hashimoto et al, 2014; Subotnik et al, 2015). Moreover, LAIs reduce the mortality rate by more than 30% because they are highly effective (Taipale et al, 2018). LAIs (such as SGAs) are most often used for the *maintenance* phase of schizophrenia, but increasingly, they're also used for the prevention of mood episodes in bipolar disorder.

❦ Key Point

If you are taking antipsychotics for relapse prevention of schizophrenia or bipolar disorder, your doctor should discuss with you the possibility of taking the medication in the form of a long-acting injectable antipsychotic (LAI). In countries other than the United States, LAIs are used more widely.

The side effects of LAIs are the same as their oral preparations, with the obvious exception of pain at the injection site. The decision regarding which LAI to choose has to do with the desired injection interval, meaning how infrequently you can receive it. While there is a large list of antipsychotics to choose from for oral use (see Table 5-5), not all antipsychotics are available as a long-acting preparation.

Table 5-5: Long-Acting Injectable Antipsychotics Available in the United States

Antipsychotic	Brand Name	Mode of Administration	Typical Injection Interval
First-Generation			
Haloperidol	Haldol® decanoate	IM	Every month
Fluphenazine	Prolixin® decanoate	IM	Every two weeks
Second-Generation			
Risperidone	Risperdal Consta® Perseris®	IM SC	Every two weeks Every month
Olanzapine*	Zyprexa Relprevv®	IM	Every two to four weeks
Paliperidone**	Invega Sustenna® Invega Trinza®	IM IM	Every month Every three months
Third-Generation			
Aripiprazole	Abilify Maintena® Aristada®	IM IM	Every month Every four, six, or eight weeks

IM = intramuscular; SC = subcutaneous
*Not widely available as it requires 3 hours of medical monitoring after the injection
**Every 6-month preparation in development

WHAT TYPES OF TALK THERAPIES (PSYCHOTHERAPY) ARE THERE?

Corinne Cather, PhD; Oliver Freudenreich, MD; and
Theodore A. Stern, MD

CHAPTER

In This Chapter

- What Are Some Different Types of Therapy?
- What Does Individual Therapy Involve?
- What Does Family Therapy Involve?
- What Is Group Therapy?
- What Do People Work on in Therapy?
- What Are the Benefits and Risks of Therapy?
- Who Is Most Likely to Benefit from Therapy?
- How Long Should I Stay in Therapy?
- How Can I Tell If My Therapy Is Working?
- How Can I Find a Therapist?
- How Can I Eventually Become My Own Therapist?

What Are Some Different Types of Therapy?

Our ideas about how therapists behave are often shaped by watching movies and TV shows that portray therapists engaging in an array of therapeutic approaches that often contradict one another. Some therapists are depicted as intrusive and others as indulgent; some provide advice, while others remain neutral; and some are open and warm, while others are distant. These fictionalized characterizations are a parody of real-life therapists and typically are not good representations of what happens in talking therapies. However, real differences do exist in how therapists conduct therapy; this is, in large part, based on how they were trained. In this section, the philosophical underpinnings of *psychodynamic therapy*, *supportive therapy*, and *cognitive-behavioral therapy* (CBT) are discussed, which broadly speaking, are three of the most commonly available approaches to therapy (see Table 6-1).

Psychotherapy as a psychological treatment for mental disorders was invented by Sigmund Freud, so it is not surprising that one of the most familiar types of therapy is *psychoanalysis* or psychodynamic therapy (also referred to as *insight-oriented* or *dynamic therapy*). These therapies are traditionally delivered intensively, sometimes more than once a week, and often over a period of many years (although briefer models have evolved). A core part of psychoanalytic/psychodynamic therapy involves helping people develop *insight* through the exploration of early life experiences and conflicts, including trauma. Psychodynamic therapists extrapolate from the person's relationship with the therapist *(transference)* to understand how he or she relates to others in their lives and believes that symptoms and disorders result from unresolved unconscious conflicts that often involve early relationships with their parents or other caregivers. Today, traditional *Freudian therapy* is no longer used in routine psychiatric care, although *psychodynamically-oriented therapy* is relatively common, particularly in certain areas of the United States.

Many therapists practice supportive therapy, which as the name implies, involves listening, responding with empathy, and generally offering support to people as they do their best to cope with their struggles. Supportive therapy is an amalgamation of different types of therapy, including *person-centered therapy*, a therapy developed by Carl Rogers, which has underlying principles of unconditional positive regard, therapist authenticity, and empathic understanding. Many of these principles overlap with characteristics of a strong *therapeutic alliance* (the relationship between the client and therapist), which is a robust predictor of the degree to which therapy is helpful, regardless of the type of psychotherapy (Flückiger et al, 2018).

CBT is a structured and directive approach to therapy that combines disorder-specific *psychoeducation* with strategies to modify maladaptive patterns of thinking or behavior that are conceptualized as causing, exacerbating, or maintaining the psychological symptoms that are distressing. These approaches are often *manualized therapies*, which means that therapists and clients each follow a specific workbook that has been designed for a specific disorder. Several types of therapy have grown out of CBT, including *dialectical-behavior therapy* (DBT) and *acceptance and commitment therapy* (ACT). DBT was designed to address emotional dysregulation, unstable relationships, thoughts of suicide, and non-suicidal self-harm behaviors, particularly for people with a history of traumatic experiences. DBT teaches distress-tolerance skills, including *mindfulness*, which is designed to help people level their emotions and sharpen their interpersonal-effectiveness skills, with the ultimate goal of improving the quality of their relationships and emotional experiences. Like DBT, ACT focuses on teaching mindfulness and disconnecting (or *"defusing"*) thoughts from action, or in other words, the principle that thoughts and impulses do not require action. Central principles of ACT include clarifying one's values in life and learning to evaluate actions in relation to these values. For example, if your most important value is to be a good parent, you might work with the ACT therapist to evaluate whether a particular emotional response or behavior (such as worrying or drinking alcohol) is moving you closer to (or further away from) the goal of being a good parent.

In reality, practitioners often employ strategies from an assortment of psychotherapy schools, so the most common type of therapist is one who identifies as *eclectic*, meaning that the therapist draws techniques from a number of therapy traditions. However, some therapists adhere more strictly to the philosophical underpinnings of their training and more clearly identify as practicing a particular type of therapy. The educated consumer should ask therapists about their practices, which type of therapy they provide, and how that therapy will be structured, and the consumer should think about the fit between what the therapist can provide and what the consumer is looking for at that point in time. It can also be useful for consumers to review the research on a specific type of therapy for their presenting problem or *diagnosis*.

Table 6-1: Comparison of Therapy Types

	How Does Therapy Produce Positive Change?	Therapist Role	Client Role	Uses a Therapy Manual?	Time-Limited
Psychodynamic therapy	Resolution of unconscious conflicts and the promotion of self-awareness	Therapist asks questions to evoke affect and assist you to make interpretations	Open to exploring past and present	No	No
Supportive therapy	Improved self-esteem and *inter-personal effectiveness* through support and guidance	Therapist adopts a helpful and supportive stance	Directs the topic of therapy	No	No
Cognitive-behavioral therapy	Identification and modification of maladaptive patterns of thought and behavior	Therapist is active and has a role in setting agenda, assigning home-work between sessions, and systematically monitoring progress	In collabo-ration with the therapist, you set the agenda and homework practice between sessions	Yes	Yes

> ### 🌿 Key Point
>
> The form that psychotherapy takes differs based on the therapist's training. Psychodynamic therapists believe it is important to gain insight into unconscious conflicts and desires. Supportive therapists believe people benefit from an encouraging relationship with a therapist who provides support and helps you think through your life's difficulties. Cognitive-behavioral therapists work on addressing distress by modifying patterns of thinking and behavior that are not adaptive as a way of increasing interpersonal effectiveness and decreasing associated distress. Whereas CBT targets more accessible thoughts, acceptance and commitment therapies target your relationship to your thoughts *(metacognition)*. DBT has been applied most effectively to decrease self-harm and thoughts of suicide and teaches skills to modulate intense and *labile* emotional responses.

What Does Individual Therapy Involve?

The structure and content of individual therapy sessions looks different depending on the type of therapy that you are accessing, although there are some commonalities, which are emphasized here according to the phase of therapy (early, middle, or late).

Typically, the early phase of therapy involves a review of the history of the problem for which you are seeking therapy. The therapist's goal is to assess the underlying risk factors and stressors that were apparent when the difficulties developed. This can be more easily accomplished when you present for therapy at or around the time of your first episode of *depression, mania,* or *psychosis,* though it is more complicated when you are coming for therapy after living with a *serious mental illness* (SMI) for many years, and the goals in this case might be quite different. For example, moving away from home, using alcohol or other drugs, having a disrupted sleep schedule, and experiencing interpersonal stress associated with making new friends, are common risk factors associated with developing a first episode of psychosis or *bipolar disorder* in a young adult. In this case, the reason you are seeking therapy is quite clear because you might have experienced a first hospitalization or a disruption in school or work because of uncharacteristic or unsafe behavior. However, if you have a longer history of illness, the question becomes "Why now?" or in other words, what is the reason that you are seeking therapy at this point in time? Have you recently experienced a worsening of *auditory hallucinations*? And if so, what could explain that? Often, *symptom* exacerbations are related to one or more of several factors, including changes in medication or medication *adherence,* changes in support (such as a move or decreased contact with family), increased use of alcohol or other drugs, or changes in the ability to employ coping strategies that were formerly effective. What emerges from this early phase of therapy is a way of conceptualizing your current difficulties together with the identification of your strengths and internal and external resources that you can optimize.

Also, patterns of thinking and behaving emerge that may help to manage your difficulties in the short term but that are hypothesized to maintain or perpetuate current distress or symptoms.

Another key task of the early phase of therapy involves orienting you to the treatment, which includes a discussion of therapy expectations. Perhaps not surprisingly, therapy outcomes are better if you hold more positive expectations about the potential benefits of therapy *(therapy outcome expectancies)* (Constantino et al, 2018) and if you believe that the amount of effort you put into therapy will make a difference in terms of how much you will benefit from therapy (known as *control expectancies*) (Delsignore and Schnyder, 2007). Related to this is establishing agreed-upon goals of treatment, which can include goal setting around the reduction of specific symptoms, behaviors, or patterns of relating to others, or it can include the increase in positive emotions, enjoyment of life, and relationships. At this stage of therapy, long-term goals are often broken down into short- and medium-term goals; for example, a rule of thumb is to identify short-term goals that will take a week, medium-term goals that will take about a month, and long-term goals that will take two to three months. This process can help avoid setting unrealistic goals for the short term, which can help buffer against the frustration and loss of self-esteem that might have resulted from previously unsuccessful attempts to attain goals. For example, it is not uncommon for a person with recently-diagnosed schizophrenia who has not been socializing for several months with anyone outside of their family to set a goal of finding a girlfriend, or for someone with bipolar disorder who has not completed college to set a goal of becoming a high-level executive. These are fine goals, but they might require incremental progress on several subordinate goals (such as developing social skills, leaving the house, retraining attention for absorbing college-level course material, or successfully passing a single class) before they are achievable.

After goal setting and conceptualization of the difficulties that have impeded goal attainment, the middle phase of therapy shifts to developing strategies to respond differently, with the goal of getting better results. For example, if you are experiencing paranoia and depression associated with schizophrenia, you might understandably respond to those experiences by isolating from others, which in the short-term, might decrease anxiety and paranoia, but in the long-term, might make it more difficult to function in the world, to feel good about yourself, and to experience positive social interactions. In turn, this reinforces patterns of paranoia and depressive thinking. CBT and related therapies, in particular, focus on monitoring and tracking progress toward the goals that are identified in therapy on an ongoing basis and emphasizes the role of practicing skills between sessions through collaborative decisions about homework assignments. These types of strategies also tend to emphasize education about the core symptoms of the disorder and key principles for its optimal management; this helps you make informed decisions about how best to manage your experience.

The key goals of the late phase of therapy are to continue to refine skills and techniques learned in therapy, to consolidate these gains, and to anticipate and plan for staying well. Schizophrenia and bipolar disorder are, in most cases, lifelong conditions that carry a risk of *relapse* that needs to be managed effectively. The specific skills learned in therapy can be useful in accomplishing a goal that is often shared by you, family members, and therapists—that of staying out of the hospital and staying well.

⅍ Key Point

Important tasks of the early phase of therapy include conceptualization of the antecedents of the symptoms or problems that prompted you to seek therapy, an orientation to treatment to clarify and perhaps modulate, treatment *expectancies,* and an identification of the goals of therapy. The middle phase of therapy focuses on the identification, implementation, and evaluation of new and effective strategies for managing emotions, experiences, symptoms, and relationships. Some therapies (such as CBT) are more structured than others (such as supportive and dynamic therapies) and use standardized tools, such as symptom measures to assess progress toward therapy goals, as well as clear homework assignments between sessions. The final phase of therapy focuses on consolidation of what was learned in therapy and development of strategies to maintain gains.

What Does Family Therapy Involve?

Family therapy is one of the most effective and underutilized tools for recovery from SMI. Family therapy and family psychoeducation markedly decrease the risk of relapse (perhaps by as much as 50%), though despite this, it is rarely used in the United States (Dixon et al, 1999). Reasons for this include a lack of trained family therapy providers; discomfort with sharing what is often considered private or sensitive information with one's family (think about how differently we think about this in terms of cardiac or cancer care); misconceptions around how privacy is handled in family therapy (see Table 6-2); and early models of therapy (which were ultimately criticized for blaming the family for causing the mental illness). Some of this was related to research that is now quite old (from the 1960s), showing that high-emotional expressivity (high EE), a tendency for there to be high levels of criticism or emotional overinvolvement in families, and strongly predicted higher levels of relapse among people with longer histories of illness who lived with families (but that did not predict relapse among those who did not live with family). An important contribution to the field was made when the study methodology was revisited. Researchers were able to demonstrate that high EE developed in families as they struggled with a challenging illness, so it was a cause rather than a result of stress from facing a difficult illness (McFarlane and Cook, 2007).

> ### ⅍ Key Point
>
> High-intensity emotions, worry, and attempts to micromanage one another can be the result of families' attempts to cope with very difficult situations. It is a rare family who can remain calm, hopeful, and loving in the face of adversity; distressed families need help (and not criticism) to play a positive role in the recovery of their relatives with SMI.

Table 6-2: Potential Privacy Concerns in Family Therapy

Myth	Reality
"My therapist is going to go behind my back and talk with my family." (client concern)	Therapists are not able to share information with family members that you have not given explicit permission to share. Exceptions to this include when you are at imminent risk of harm or when you share knowledge that you are aware that someone who cannot protect themselves (such as a minor, disabled adult, or elderly person) has been harmed or that a specific person is at risk of being harmed.
"My therapist will force me to include certain family members that I do not want to include." (client concern)	You need to give your permission to include specific family members in any family therapy you are taking part of. Families or couples have the right to pursue family therapy on their own if you do not want to be involved, though once you are involved, you have the final say about who takes part.
"The family therapist will take their (the person with mental illness) side, and we are afraid to say the truth in front of (the person with mental illness) because he or she will get upset."	A skilled family therapist will help create a non-blaming space where people are permitted to share different perspectives without leading to arguments and hard feelings. Also, it is important to understand that although therapists do not have the right to communicate information to the family members without your permission, family members always have the right to communicate information to the therapist.

An important tenet of family therapy is that intervening at the level of the family system versus exclusively at the level of the individual (as in individual therapy) will produce better results. New models have arisen and they are now more commonly used when a family affected by SMI accesses family therapy. These include family psychoeducation and *behavioral family therapy* (sometimes also called *family focused therapy*), which may be delivered in either single-family or *multi-family group therapy* format. Behavioral family therapy can be provided in either a single-family format or a multi-family group models, which include multiple families and clients participating together. Although the benefits of single and multi-family group therapy have been roughly equivalent in terms of client-level outcomes (Bradley et al, 2006; Dyck et al, 2000) and multi-family group programs are more difficult to establish because of logistics, there might be some benefits to family members and people related to receiving support in multi-family groups from other families that are facing similar challenges together. Another possible benefit of multi-family group models is the ability for *inter-family communication*, which is the idea that a client might be able to hear something said by a parent of another family, but not by his own parent.

As in individual therapy, family therapy models often begin with an assessment of the current difficulties in terms of how they are affecting the family system. Typically, the therapist meets individually with each family member to hear each person's perspective on the challenges and strengths of their family; individual goals, which might be unrelated to the family member with SMI; and goals for their family relationships. Then families begin meeting together with the therapist. Each participant is encouraged to speak from his or her own experience (versus speaking for others in the family), and a common early goal of family work is to increase shared positive family activities. Later goals include learning more about the illness and its optimal treatment, as well as skills training, specifically in the areas of *problem-solving skills training* and *communication skills training*. (See Tables 6-3 and 6-4 for examples of these skills.)

Table 6-3: Family Problem-Solving/Goal-Setting

Steps of Family Problem-Solving/Goal-Setting		
Rationale: Solving problems or approaching goals with a structured approach often leads to better outcomes.		
Framework: Everyone's input is important.		
Step 1	Family members discuss the problem or goal and come to a consensus on what the problem or goal is.	"John is waking up after 1 p.m. every day."
Step 2	Brainstorm (at least three) possible solutions/approaches.	Go to bed earlier. Schedule a trip to the gym at 10 a.m., three times each week. Do errands with Mom in the morning.
Step 3	Evaluate the pros and cons of each solution.	**Pros** • Might be less tired in the morning. • Wants to go to the gym because he used to do this. • Might feel good to help with errands, and it would be good to get out. **Cons** • Enjoy staying up late. • Not likely to wake up at 10 a.m. • Mom might get frustrated waiting for me.

Steps of Family Problem-Solving/Goal-Setting (continued)		
Step 4	Choose the best solution or combination of solutions.	Plan to go to the gym on Mondays, Wednesdays, and Fridays with Mom at 11:30 a.m.
Step 5	Decide what is needed to implement the solution.	Set alarm, have gym clothes ready, and Mom will have coffee for me for the car ride.
Step 6	Evaluate how well the solution worked at the next family meeting and troubleshoot any difficulties.	Got to the gym on Wednesday at noon and on Friday at 3 p.m.

Table 6-4: Family Communication Skills Training Targets

Skill	Example	Tips	What Can Go Wrong
Expressing a positive feeling.	"You made me so happy this morning when I found you made me hot coffee."	• Look at the person. • Use a kind voice tone and expression. • Be specific about what he or she did. • Tell the person how it made you feel.	• Be genuine. You do not want a person to feel you are being condescending or false.
Expressing a positive request.	"I would appreciate it if you took out the garbage and recycling before 7 a.m. tomorrow."	• Look at the person. • Make a specific request. • Tell the person how it would make you feel if he or she completed the request.	• Keep it simple. Do not load request on top of request. Make sure your request is reasonable for the person's current capacity.
Expressing a negative feeling.	"I was upset and worried when you did not come home until 2 a.m. In the future, I would like you to call me by 11 p.m. if you are going to be later than midnight."	• Look at the person. • Use a serious tone of voice. • Tell the person specifically what he or she did and how it made you feel. • Make a specific request for how you would like the person to handle the situation differently in the future.	• Avoid name-calling (such as, "I don't know if you were just being selfish or lazy." • Avoid comparisons (such as "Your sister is only 14 and she does her chores without my asking." • Pick your battles wisely—concern about safety need to be a high priority.

continued

Skill	Example	Tips	What Can Go Wrong
Compromise and negotiation.	"I am displeased that I do not get to see you at all during the day because you are sleeping late and staying in your room. I hear your perspective that it makes you feel uncomfortable to come out of your room and be with the family. What if we spent one hour together in the evenings either playing cards or watching a show together? What do you think?"	• Explain your viewpoint. Listen to the other person's viewpoint. Repeat back what you heard to show understanding. Suggest a compromise. • Be open to talking over other possible compromises.	• Avoid getting caught up in a cycle of criticism/defensiveness. • Focus on the solution more than the problem.

National Association of Mental Illness (NAMI) Family-to-Family is an important, widely available, and free resource for families in their local communities. (See https://www.nami.org/Find-Your-Local-NAMI to find a program near you.) This is a structured, 12-week, and in-person educational course that is led by family members who have been affected by a family member with SMI and who have been trained to conduct this course. In this model, family members participate without the person with SMI. Participation in NAMI Family-to-Family has decreased the subjective burden and distress and has improved empowerment, mental health knowledge, self-care, and family functioning (Dixon et al, 2011)—all things that improve recovery (although the benefits at the level of the person with SMI have yet to be identified).

A word about siblings is important here: Siblings are often a neglected resource in the treatment of people with SMI. Whereas parents sometimes walk on eggshells, siblings can often say things more directly to people with SMI and get results; also, siblings are closer in age than are parents, so they can be more acceptable companions for facilitating social activities and assisting with school goals, such as help with accessing online course materials. Particularly as parents age, siblings might struggle with their role in supporting their sister or brother with SMI, and laying the groundwork for helping siblings understand how to achieve optimal recovery is invaluable.

What Is Group Therapy?

Social skills training and *illness management* and *recovery skills training* are all effective when delivered in group settings. Social skills training involves breaking skills into smaller components to communicate with others effectively. For example, you could role-play initiating a conversation and then use more role-play to practice and refine the skill with positive and corrective feedback from the group. Social skills training is the most effective treatment to date for *negative symptoms* of schizophrenia (Kurtz and Mueser, 2008) and it has been widely implemented in the Veterans Administration (VA) setting, although it is not available in most community settings. Illness management and recovery is also a skills-based intervention that has been effective when delivered in either group or individual settings. (See https://store.samhsa.gov/product/Illness-Management-and-Recovery-Evidence-Based-Practices-EBP-KIT/sma09-4462.) Illness management and recovery entails a systematic review of areas of satisfaction in one's life to identify personal goals and then provides suggestions for coping and for skills that a person might use to remediate areas where life could be improved.

What Do People Work on in Therapy?

The goals of individual therapy often include making sense out of what has happened, figuring out ways to maintain a positive self-image despite the illness and life disruptions (such as an interrupted education) and losses (such as friends and aspirations). Other goals include developing coping strategies for specific symptoms, preventing relapse and staying well, and establishing goals related to continued growth and living one's life more fully despite having what can be a very difficult illness. Broad goals of effective family interventions include illness education, support, and family training in how to communicate, solve problems, and attain goals.

Most people live under the assumption that they will be mentally and physically healthy throughout most of their lives. The average age-of-onset for SMI is sometime between 16 and 30 years, with men typically showing an earlier age-of-onset. When a chronic illness affects a young person, the first reaction is often complete disbelief and at times, serious mental health conditions are overlooked and attributed initially to drugs or to a developmental phase. Once the illness is recognized, therapy can help you make sense out of the experience and offer an opportunity to experience a sense of control over the illness. Also, therapy helps address any misplaced guilt or shame that surrounds your responsibility for having the illness.

There is an enormous societal stigma associated with SMI that is important to acknowledge because it greatly affects the experience of people and families who have SMI. Reduced social support to both you and your family is common following an illness. (Again, you should contrast this with what happens when a family is affected by cancer.) *Internalized stigma*, which is also referred to as *self-stigma*, occurs when a person diagnosed with a SMI applies negative stereotypes about mental illness (such as being dangerous or unable to recover) to their own thinking about themselves (Corrigan et al, 2006; Ritsher et al, 2003). These beliefs are important to identify and modify in therapy. Of note, the longer people with schizophrenia go untreated, the more internalized and self-stigmatized views they have (Mueser et al, 2020), which suggests that one way untreated illness can lead to poorer recovery outcomes is through damage to self-esteem.

Illness management goals include optimizing your ability to cope with specific symptoms, such as anxiety, depression, *hallucinations, paranoia*, and negative symptoms; maintaining a regular sleep/wake schedule (particularly important in the case of mania); and identifying and achieving life goals.

> #### ⅍ Key Point
>
> Broadly speaking, therapy goals for SMI include learning about the illness and its optimal management and developing the necessary skills to engage in these management strategies. Recovery from a SMI often involves rebuilding one's life and self-image; therapy can also help with these goals.

What Are the Benefits and Risks of Therapy?

Some types of therapy have been studied more than others. Cognitive-behaviorally oriented therapies, in particular, have been researched fairly extensively in schizophrenia and have been shown to (in combination with use of *antipsychotic* medication) have positive effects on psychotic symptoms, negative symptoms, and general symptoms like depression and anxiety (Burns et al, 2014).

Cognitive-behaviorally-informed therapies tend to be well-tolerated; individual and family interventions aligned with this model are a key component of the *evidence-based practice* for *first-episode psychosis*. A centerpiece of *gold standard* interventions for first-episode psychosis is a focus on identifying and strengthening *resilience* (also known as being able "to bounce back" and build on one's individual strengths following adversity). *Coordinated specialty care* is a model that includes supported employment and education services (specialized services to assist with school and work goals); medication management; individual resilience therapy and family psychoeducation and skills training. A large, *randomized controlled trial* (RCT) of this multi-component, integrated approach to first-episode care found that this approach led to better engagement in treatment, greater symptom reduction, greater improvement in quality of life, better interpersonal relationships, and more school/work involvement (Kane et al, 2015).

As with schizophrenia, psychoeducational, cognitive-behavioral, and family-focused therapies have received the most attention in treatment outcome research for bipolar disorder. Also, *interpersonal social rhythm therapy*—a form of therapy that is focused on strategies to promote medication adherence and maintain consistency and decrease disruption in daily activities, sleep-wake cycle, and social interactions—has been studied in bipolar disorder.

Risks of therapy are often not given as much consideration as are their benefits. Like any relationship, the relationship with a therapist can impose stress or friction. It can be uncomfortable for you to talk about certain things in therapy or it might lead to feeling badly for missing appointments or not completing exercises between sessions. Sometimes, it can be difficult for you to tolerate a relationship with someone who you feel has "seen me at my worst," such as in the middle of an illness episode. You should remember that just like any service you pay for (such as personal training, massage, or haircuts), you are in control of how long you stay in therapy and whether you choose to take a break or to switch therapists. With sufficient notice, therapists also have the right to let you know that they do not feel the therapy is productive or helpful or that things have changed and they will, at some point, not be able to continue therapy.

Who Is Most Likely to Benefit from Therapy?

Probably one of the most important considerations about therapy is whether you are willing to give it a try. People who are not interested in therapy and who are unwilling to meet with a therapist at least several times to give it a try are unlikely to benefit from therapy. Like most treatments, it requires that you are a somewhat willing participant.

Most research also suggests that at least for a SMI such as bipolar disorder and schizophrenia, therapy works better in conjunction with medication than without medication. In recent years, some very prominent CBT experts have endeavored to determine whether it is safe and feasible to study whether therapy could benefit people with first episode psychosis without medication (Morrison et al, 2020). At this point, the best evidence for therapy is for people who are taking medication or who are open to starting medication shortly after starting therapy. Most therapy research in bipolar disorder has been conducted with those who are not in a manic state, and clinical experience suggests it is not possible to make headway in therapy while a person is contending with frank mania.

⁂ Key Point

Therapy requires an element of *motivation*. There is little or no benefit if you do not believe therapy will help and do not participate actively. However, because many people do not really know what therapy is like or might not have accessed a newer model of therapy, it can be a good idea to see if you would be willing to try one or two therapy sessions before making a final decision to stop therapy.

How Long Should I Stay in Therapy?

The idea of time-limited therapy is very reasonable; there is no reason that therapy needs to continue forever, particularly once the therapy goals have been met. Therapy can also be intermittent; for example, it might just be needed at times of crises. Consensus treatment guidelines provide some evidence-based recommendations on treatment lengths for both individual CBT and family therapy (Kreyenbuhl et al, 2009). CBT is recommended in either a group or individual format for 4–9 months. Ideally, family interventions should be offered for 6–9 months because these program lengths are more likely to be associated with positive outcomes. At a minimum, all families should be offered at least four sessions that are focused on psychoeducation, providing support to the family, and teaching the family basic principles of how they can help you get the best results from treatment.

How Can I Tell If My Therapy Is Working?

One of the best ways to tell if therapy is working is for you and your therapist to agree to use some way of tracking progress once you have established some agreed-upon goals. For example, a person who has a therapy goal of reducing depressive symptoms could respond to a depression scale such as the *Patient Health Questionnaire-9* (PHQ-9) at specified intervals throughout treatment and review scores to determine if the symptoms of depression are improving, staying the same, or getting worse. Several smartphone apps and online platforms (such as moodtracker.com) are available to accomplish the same thing. Some therapists routinely use methods such as this. You might also want to talk with people around you to see if they notice any differences in you since you began therapy, although you should keep in mind that these types of reports can be biased by their views of therapy. People who encouraged you to participate in therapy might see benefits, whereas those who discouraged you, might fail to see those benefits. The best plan might be to take into account all sources of information, including your general sense of whether there is improvement, your therapist's report, the report of others' close to you, and any systematically-collected data. Keep in mind, however, that it is often important to give therapy enough time to determine if it is working (or if it has some promise of working!). An adequate trial might differ according to the type of therapy you are following and to how distressed you are at the time you access therapy. A good rule of thumb is to attend at least four sessions before you make any decisions.

How Can I Find a Therapist?

One challenge is that many people do not know the differences in the training background and degrees held by various types of therapists. This is further complicated by the fact that anyone can call themselves a "therapist" or "psychotherapist." However, you should look for a therapist who is licensed, which indicates that they have met certain professional standards and are required to uphold certain ethical standards. *Psychologists* (PhDs and PsyDs) and *licensed independent clinical social workers* (LICSWs) are required to undergo more extensive training than *licensed mental health counselors* (LMHCs). Sometimes, you might have the opportunity to have therapy with a trainee who is receiving supervision from a licensed person, which the trainee is required to discuss with you. You have to weigh several factors in your decision, including the level of training and the years of experience. However, the degree to which you feel a connection with a therapist—part of the therapeutic alliance—is a key determinant of outcomes, so this might be one of the most important factors to take into consideration.

Finding a doctor can be challenging; finding a therapist can be even more so because of a few factors, including a limited number of therapists with experience with schizophrenia or bipolar disorder (compared to, say, anxiety or depression) and stricter insurance limitations for therapy (what insurers refer to as "behavioral health") relative to medical health. If you already have a care provider who is prescribing medication, a good place to start would be to ask this person to refer you to a therapist. It is often helpful to have "*integrated care*," which is when the therapist and prescribing care provider can communicate easily and coordinate their care. This enables them to respond to any symptoms or problems in a concerted way. However, if you do not already have someone to prescribe psychiatric medication, you can start with your primary care physician's office as a resource. These offices often keep a list of therapist referrals. Word-of-mouth can also be a good way to find a therapist, for example, if you are participating in a NAMI Family-to-Family class, you may want to find out from other families if they have seen or heard of a good individual or family therapist. Local *community mental health centers* (CMHCs), are clinics that are mandated to provide behavioral health care to people who live within a certain radius. You can search the internet for therapists in your town or county or call the local CMHC to ask to become a new therapy client. Another option is to ask your insurer for a list of therapists who accept your insurance or use internet-based sites, such as Psychology Today or the Association of Cognitive and Behavioral Therapy, to identify therapists in your local area.

How Can I Eventually Become My Own Therapist?

Becoming your own therapist requires developing an awareness of what you believed helped you during your therapy and your knowledge of how to replicate what was helpful in the course of regular life at times when you do not have a therapist prompting you to use these techniques or skill. During therapy, it can be useful for you to keep written records of the skills you are working on, how and when you implemented them, and how you overcame any challenges or obstacles to doing so. (When you think about it, it does not make a lot of sense that only the therapist would keep notes of the therapy sessions!) Once you have attained some benefit from therapy, it is typical to space out therapy sessions to occur less frequently, so for example, once-a-week therapy might shift to once every other week. The goals during this phase of therapy could include your maintaining the weekly therapy session as a check-in with yourself. For example, you could even put this in your calendar as an appointment during which time you would replicate what you did in therapy. For example, check to see if your symptoms are better, worse, or the same, and identify whether you made the desired progress on the goals you set the previous week, as well as modify or set new goals for the coming week or review a previously learned skill.

WHAT IS THE ROLE OF PSYCHIATRIC REHABILITATION?

Corinne Cather, PhD; Oliver Freudenreich, MD; and
Theodore A. Stern, MD

CHAPTER

In This Chapter

- Why Should I Consider Psychiatric Rehabilitation?

- What Are the Underlying Principles of Psychiatric Rehabilitation?

- Where Is Psychiatric Rehabilitation Provided?

- What Types of Psychiatric Rehabilitation Services Are There?

- What Is Supported Employment and Education?

- How Should I Decide Whether to Disclose My Mental Illness History to Schools or Potential Employers?

- How Do I Decide Whether to Apply for Supplemental Security Income/ Social Security Disability Insurance?

- What Are Some Rehabilitation Options for Cognitive Difficulties?

- What Are the Benefits of Psychiatric Rehabilitation?

- When Should I Start Psychiatric Rehabilitation?

- How Long Should I Be in Psychiatric Rehabilitation?

- How Do I Access Psychiatric Rehabilitation?

Why Should I Consider Psychiatric Rehabilitation?

If you had knee surgery, you would not be surprised to receive advice and a referral for *physical therapy* (PT) from your physician to facilitate your healing and to gradually increase your muscle strength and flexibility. Another benefit of PT might be meeting other people receiving PT who had a similar operation and hearing about their injuries and recoveries, which could provide companionship, help with setting realistic expectations, and hope. *Psychosocial rehabilitation* or *psychiatric rehabilitation* ("rehabilitation" for short in this chapter) is a set of practices that are intended to optimize functioning and wellbeing and are used in conjunction with psychiatric treatment. The goal is to use therapy to strengthen, and to the extent possible, remediate or compensate for deficits that were affected by *serious mental illness* (SMI). Mental health issues can cause *symptoms* that adversely affect functioning or have indirect effects, such as eroding your social or school/work skills when you lose opportunities to practice these skills. Rehabilitation resources help rebuild these skills and provide support and opportunities for you to pursue your goals. Ideally, rehabilitation service providers understand how mental health issues affect life, functioning, skills, and self-confidence, and they provide a welcoming atmosphere where effective support is offered.

What Are the Underlying Principles of Psychiatric Rehabilitation?

Psychiatric rehabilitation encourages empowerment, a belief in human rights, and *therapeutic optimism*. As such, psychiatric rehabilitation often involves a focus on treatment, choice, respect for autonomy, and positive expectations for recovery. The services offered are based on your goals and values, and they are designed to be flexible and non-hierarchical, and to facilitate social inclusion.

The *stress-vulnerability model* (Zubin and Spring, 1977) provides a framework for thinking about the role of psychiatric rehabilitation services for SMI. This model identifies five key facilitators of recovery: engaging in productive and enjoyable activities; utilizing positive social support; developing effective coping strategies; taking medications; and refraining from use of harmful substances (see Figure 7-1). In accordance with this model, modern psychiatric rehabilitation services provide potential pathways to develop social connections and assist with securing employment and working on educational goals. They might also offer specific skills training, such as strategic management of anxiety or classes that teach how to increase social connections.

Psychiatric rehabilitation services arose in tandem with the recovery movement. Perhaps, in part, because of this history, a clear separation between psychiatric rehabilitation services and treatment often exists. Although providers of psychiatric care might recommend psychiatric rehabilitation services (and a referral from your provider might be necessary to access these services), in practice, there is often no further communication between psychiatric providers and rehabilitation services. This is unfortunate because it represents a missed opportunity for broad support for your rehabilitation and treatment goals.

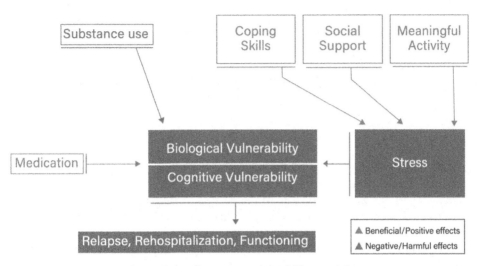

Figure 7-1: The stress-vulnerability model.

☆ Key Point

Psychiatric rehabilitation and treatment are separate yet equally important and complementary components of care for SMI. Psychiatric rehabilitation focuses on function and role outcomes, whereas treatment focuses on symptomatic relief.

Where Is Psychiatric Rehabilitation Provided?

Psychiatric rehabilitation can be provided in a variety of settings, such as *specialized rehabilitation centers*, *day treatment*, clubhouses, *drop-in centers*, *private residential settings*, or state-funded *vocational support agencies*.

Specialized Psychiatric Rehabilitation Centers

Model psychiatric rehabilitation centers exist across the country; they are dedicated to the psychosocial rehabilitation of people with SMI. Typically, these centers function in collaboration with an *academic center* and are often funded by federal grants provided by agencies, such as the *National Institute on Disability and Independent Living and Rehabilitation Research* (NIDILRR); or organizations such as The Boston University Center for Psychiatric Rehabilitation (see https://cpr.bu.edu/). Less often, these centers are funded by a combination of hospital support, research grants, and private foundation support, such as The

Lieber Recovery Clinic in New York (see https://www.columbiadoctors.org/specialties/ psychiatry-psychology/our-services/lieber-recovery-clinic). In addition to providing opportunities for developing a social network, these centers can provide access to state-of-the-art psychiatric rehabilitation services, such as *cognitive remediation, evidence-based employment*, and educational support. Services can be provided at no charge, be billed to your insurance provider, or may include some offerings that require paying privately or applying for scholarship funds to defray costs.

Day Treatment

Day treatment is often accessed following a hospitalization, which means many people enter day treatment during an *acute* exacerbation of illness. Typically, day treatment is offered for part of a weekday (such as 10 a.m. to 2 p.m.). Like a *partial hospitalization program*, day treatment might be offered at a psychiatric treatment center and might be paid for by insurance. Unlike a partial hospitalization program, which is typically offered for a limited period (up to three weeks), day treatment may be available for several months or more. Sometimes, day treatment includes vocational support.

Clubhouses and Drop-In Centers

Clubhouses were originally formed by patients (during the era of *deinstitutionalization* in the 1960s and 1970s) after they were discharged from state hospitals and had no place to go. Many clubhouses have unique names. The first club house (Fountain House) was established in New York City. Clubhouses are often large (with up to several hundred of people attending them each year), predominantly peer-run, and designed to provide opportunities for socialization, learning, and collaborative work related to running the clubhouse. (See https://clubhouse-intl.org/what-we-do/what-clubhouses-do/.) They tend to be open during the day from 9 a.m. to 5 p.m., five or six days a week. Clubhouses have no fees and being employed is not a requirement. Often, residential programs provide transportation to the club house. Some clubhouses sponsor weekend trips to a variety of places, such as museums, theater/movies, or hiking trails. Clubhouses often serve free/ discounted breakfast and/or lunch that is largely prepared, served, and cleaned up by the members. Historically, clubhouses offered *transitional employment* options, which are temporary jobs (often paid below market value) created for club house members. Although these transitional jobs were often created to fill a person with pride and to translate into more permanent employment, they did not produce this result (Becker et al, 1998). While many people did well while they had the jobs, they were disappointed once the positions failed to translate into longer-term employment.

For example, some educational support resources (such as classes on how to use a computer or how to apply for a job) are offered at clubhouses. Clubhouses tend to have community meetings regarding running the club house democratically. Although membership in some clubhouses requires a referral from a provider or from a pre-established relationship with an organization, such as a *Department of Mental Health* (DMH), clubhouses tend to provide a place that is distinct from the treatment system, with minimal barriers to access for people with lived experience of mental health challenges.

In recent years, the clubhouse model has been threatened by funding cuts and by an emphasis on *evidence-based practices* for employment (such as *individual placement and support/supported employment and education*—discussed below) that have gained popularity. Perhaps in response to this trend, some efforts have been made to modernize clubhouses, with a greater emphasis placed on providing opportunities for a structured club house day and an increase in *peer support* and the number of *recovery coaches* in the club house setting. In some states, clubhouses have been augmented or replaced by smaller, exclusively peer-run rehabilitation services. In Massachusetts, these are called *Recovery Learning Communities* (RLCs) (https://www.mass.gov/service-details/recovery-learning-communities).

The primary challenge to engaging people in clubhouses and drop-in centers is resistance to being around people with mental disorders and the perception/reality that other members of the organization will be dissimilar to you in terms of age, race/ethnicity, and/or life experience. Unfortunately, options are limited for people who are 18–25 years old and who are seeking youth-friendly initiatives linked to coordinated care for *first-episode psychosis*. Transportation can also be a barrier; unlike medical visits—for which physicians can assist with the application for free transportation for Medicaid/Medicare recipients— transportation to psychiatric rehabilitation is not covered by insurance.

Private Residential Settings/Therapeutic Communities

These are *private pay* residential options that offer coordinated treatment and psychiatric rehabilitation support in a residential setting (sometimes, but not always in a beautiful country/farm setting). They are often expensive and not feasible for most people and their families who are affected by SMI. Moreover—and perhaps somewhat controversially— many families pay a lot of money for such programs or communities to provide their family members with the best care, yet they come to regret their decisions. This might have to do with the fact that SMIs are chronic illnesses that require a plan for lifelong management, often lasting many decades, and these programs are focused on short-term management or are not affordable when long-term care is needed, even for those with significant financial resources. Directories of these programs are available at https://artausa.org/residential-mental-health-directory/); you should also take into consideration the level of expertise of the staff and how the program fits your goals and manifestations. You should also seek to determine what resources are available to help you transition from the program to another living situation.

State-Funded Vocational Support Agencies

All states have vocational agencies to support unemployed people who are seeking employment services or job training. Most states also offer specialized services to provide employment or job training to people with disabilities; however, the degree to which these agencies can support you given your mental health challenges is highly variable.

What Types of Psychiatric Rehabilitation Services Are There?

It can be difficult to distinguish psychiatric rehabilitation from treatment. Some people consider specialized therapeutic interventions, such as *recovery-oriented cognitive behavior therapy* (Grant et al, 2018) for schizophrenia and *social skills training*, to be more like psychiatric rehabilitation services than a treatment. (See Chapter 6 for a discussion of CBT and SST.) In the following sections, we discuss interventions that are focused on improving outcomes for work and school, including supported employment and education, cognitive remediation, and *cognitive adaptation therapy* (CAT).

What Is Supported Employment and Education?

In the early 1990s, Becker and Drake developed a model of supported employment and education (SEE) for people with SMI (Drake and Becker, 1996) that was later systematized and shown to be more effective than comparison employment approaches in multiple *controlled trials* (Bond, 2004; Crowther et al, 2001). The approach has been further articulated and expanded to include support for educational goals. It resulted in superior outcomes for work and school for people with first-episode psychosis in a large *randomized controlled trial* (RCT) (Kane et al, 2015; Mueser et al, 2015).

Key principles and practices of supported employment/education include *zero exclusion*; a focus on competitive work (versus volunteer work) for people interested in working; integration with treatment; respect for clients' personal preferences (in terms of job match and *disclosure*); education about *Supplemental Security Income* (SSI) and work; assessment that does not delay rapid initiation of a job search; and provision of follow-along supports. (See Table 7-1 for the characteristics of high quality SEE.)

Table 7-1: Characteristics of High-Quality Supported Education and Employment Services

• Don't exclude anyone with SMI who wants to work (regardless of perceived readiness, substance use, symptoms)
• Have the goal of obtaining competitive work for those interested in working
• Integrate with psychiatric treatment
• Respect patients' personal preferences in terms of job match and disclosure (and provide education about the pros and cons of disclosure)
• Provide education about the pros/cons of receiving *entitlements*, such as SSI or SSDI
• Include an assessment that does not delay rapid initiation of a job search
• Provide follow-along supports (such as a SEE specialist who coordinates with the job supervisor and provides coaching on [or off] the work site)

Zero exclusion refers to the practice of offering supported employment and education to anyone with SMI, not solely to those who are taking medication or judged to be "ready" for this service (based on symptoms or degree of *motivation* for work or school). All people should be offered this service; anyone interested in pursuing school or work should be eligible to receive this service without having to "jump through hoops," such as attending group orientations or suffering through a burdensome application process.

> ### ❧ Key Point
>
> Anyone who expresses an interest in working should be offered *vocational rehabilitation*. Modern vocational rehabilitation trains people (with support) in real workplaces (the *place and train model*) and no longer focuses on extensive preparation for work (the *train and place model*).

Integration with treatment refers to coordination between the SEE specialist and the treatment team. This integration allows your goals for school and work to be a central treatment goal. As each team member gains experience with you and learns more about you, your interests, and your talents, more ideas can be generated around how to best realize your educational and work goals. Integration with treatment also permits the SEE to support you and to coordinate with the team around your symptoms, side effects, and/or issues of medication *non-adherence* that are interfering with your performance at work or school.

Learning about your preferences requires an assessment of your goals, interests, and strengths, as well as your past work/school history, including successes and difficulties. Although assessment should be thorough and ongoing, it should not delay a rapid job search. Instead, it is important to "strike while the iron is hot" and quickly move to the job/school search and application process so as not to lose momentum during the assessment phase. Throughout this process, ambitious goals should not be discouraged (such as going to medical school) and you should think about a starting point that would put you on the path to achieving something ambitious (such as becoming an EMT or taking a biology course). Alternatively, you should think about what can be learned from this ambitious goal, such as whether there are other ways to achieve your core goal. For instance, if your goal is to go to medical school because you want to help people, perhaps there are other ways you could help people aside from going to medical school.

Job development is a big piece of the supported employment specialist's job, which involves matching you with potential employers in the community. This means learning about your interests (such as animals) and then visiting potential employers in the area (such as veterinary offices, pet supply stores, shelters, kennels, and wildlife refuges) to develop a relationship, learn about job openings, and, with your permission, provide information to the potential employer about whether the job development specialist thinks you fit the employer's needs. Outside of the United States, *affirmative businesses (social firms)* provide a model of hiring people with psychiatric illnesses to provide a service. This has been enacted on a large scale for people with developmental disabilities in the United States (such as working in grocery stores), but there has been less traction for this model for people with psychiatric illnesses, perhaps due to stigma. This is a missed opportunity because people with SMI who want to work are often very motivated to succeed.

How Should I Decide Whether to Disclose My Mental Illness History to Schools or Potential Employers?

Considering your preferences for work or school and for how you want to handle disclosure of your past or present mental health history is an important piece of SEE. Although research has suggested that people who disclose their mental health history work longer (Detore et al, 2019), this remains an individual decision and your views on whether to disclose will change over the course of your school or work experiences. Disclosure can protect people under the *Americans with Disabilities Act* (ADA) by requiring that reasonable accommodations be provided to the student or employee who discloses a mental health condition. However, fewer protections are provided during probationary work periods. In educational settings, such as high school or college, it is usually recommended that students disclose their mental health history and ask for accommodations because this information is protected under federal law and doing so offers certain types of assistance (which do not need to be used), such as extended time on tests, a reduced-distraction testing environment, note-taking help, and tutoring. Most, if not all, colleges and universities in the United States offer student support services. For students in public elementary or high school settings, parents must request a "504 plan evaluation" in writing from the school as a first step toward initiating the process of obtaining accommodations.

How Do I Decide Whether to Apply for Supplemental Security Income/Social Security Disability Insurance?

Some people who access SEE might already be receiving benefits, such as Supplemental Security Income (SSI) or *Social Security Disability Insurance* (SSDI), and it is important to provide education about who is eligible for these benefits, the differences between them, and how work income and/or enrolling in school could affect these benefits (such as *benefits counselling*). (For more information, see www.ssa.gov/redbook/.)

Other people wonder whether they should apply for SSI or SSDI. Many people who receive entitlements of this type fear starting or restarting work because they might lose these benefits, their insurance, and/or their housing once they start working.

⅋ Key Point

Receiving entitlements/benefits, such as SSI/SSDI, can create a disincentive to work because some people fear they will lose their financial security, health insurance, and/or housing. Therefore, you should receive education and support about the facts and identify myths regarding this issue.

Sometimes, the decision about whether to apply for SSI is driven by an actual or perceived financial need to be eligible for *Medicaid*. However, many families do not know that in many states, having a SMI entitles you to remain on your parent's health insurance after the age of 26, which is when most plans require that the child no longer receive health insurance as a dependent. Historically, it has been uncommon for people who have begun receiving disability payments to transition to financial independence (Wehmeyer and Palmer, 2003). Given this and the fact that SSI is not sufficient to exceed the poverty level, the decision to begin receiving disability payments is not one to be taken lightly; when done, it can be helpful to view this as "temporary disability," so that you don't lose your focus on making your future as independent as possible.

> ### ⅍ Key Point
>
> When thinking about starting benefits, such as SSI, you should think about devising a plan for getting off these benefits as quickly as possible, so that you can achieve financial independence.

Once you obtain employment (or are accepted as a student), another key feature of SEE is to offer and provide follow-along supports. This might involve serving as a liaison between a supervisor and employee or between student support services and a student; skills training to address challenges or new demands; and/or coordination with the treatment team to address symptoms or medication issues that interfere with performance or planning.

What Are Some Rehabilitation Options for Cognitive Difficulties?

Cognitive difficulties are a core feature of schizophrenia-spectrum illnesses, such that cognitive impairments often precede the onset of illness and are associated with significant functional impairments (Corigliano et al, 2014). Similarly, difficulties with attention and concentration are common in *affective illness*, particularly during acute mood episodes. Also, *attention deficit hyperactivity disorder* (ADHD) often co-occurs with *bipolar disorder* and is associated with a worse course of illness (McIntyre et al, 2010).

Broadly speaking, there are two different rehabilitation approaches for cognitive difficulties in SMI. The first is cognitive remediation, which has the goal of restoring cognitive functions through training. The second is cognitive adaptation therapy (CAT), which has the goal of developing compensatory strategies or work-arounds for cognitive difficulties.

Cognitive remediation refers to a rehabilitation approach designed to improve cognitive functions (such as attention, working memory, and processing speed), through use of computer-based tasks that increase in difficulty as your performance on these tasks improves with practice. Cognitive remediation is sometimes combined with strategy coaching, which involves helping you optimize the strategy employed on the tasks. For example, when given a list of words to remember from different categories, it is more efficient to chunk the words into their respective categories (such as which items were vegetables and which items were pieces of clothing) than to try to remember the list of words in order. The duration and frequency of cognitive remediation programs is quite variable and might be offered three times per week for 30- to 45-minute sessions over 3 to 18 months. Cognitive remediation has been studied most often in people with schizophrenia-spectrum illnesses and has been associated with small improvements in cognition when compared to control interventions, such as video games (Glenthøj et al, 2017; Krabbendam and Aleman, 2003; Pilling et al, 2002) and somewhat stronger effects when combined with strategy coaching (McGurk et al, 2007). Although cognitive remediation as a stand-alone intervention has not improved functioning, *synergistic effects* of cognitive remediation have been combined with other psychosocial rehabilitation strategies, such as supported employment (McGurk et al, 2007; Teixeira et al, 2018).

> ### ⅍ Key Point
>
> The effects of cognitive remediation are strongest when combined with other psychiatric rehabilitation approaches, such as supported employment.

Whereas cognitive remediation is geared to restore cognitive functions, CAT aims to compensate for cognitive deficits by providing compensatory strategies or work-arounds. For example, a CAT technician might place signs, sticky notes, and/or checklists around your apartment to overcome difficulties with memory, attention, or planning. CAT works best when it is tailored to your home environment and specific challenges. For example, you might benefit from checklists that specify the order of operations required to pay bills, while someone else might do well with a system for reviewing his or her calendar for the week ahead on Sunday evenings and establishing plans for any preparations or plans required to complete their scheduled activities (such as homework, transportation planning, and emails to send prior to these appointments). CAT might be delivered by a trained technician or by a family member and it improves cognition and functioning while the interventions are in place; however, the effects are not sustained once the reminders and structure of CAT have been withdrawn (Velligan et al, 2000).

Unfortunately, high-quality cognitive rehabilitation services are difficult to access, as their availability is most often dependent on whether there is a research study that offers these services. Some *neuropsychologists* offer cognitive remediation strategy coaching that might be combined with commercially available computer software. Some *occupational therapists* and *psychologists* who specialize in either rehabilitation following a *traumatic brain injury* (TBI) or ADHD might be able to adapt these skill sets to working on cognitive rehabilitation strategies with people who have SMI, although it might take some research and creative thinking to identify these practitioners.

What Are the Benefits of Psychiatric Rehabilitation?

Work is good medicine. Consistent with the stress-vulnerability model, working is associated with improved wellbeing and fewer symptoms (Bond et al, 2001). Other benefits include the reinforcement of positive *expectancies*, such as hopeful attitudes about the potential for living well despite a serious illness; achieving developmental milestones, such as earning an educational degree, marriage, and parenting; and hope and an active stance in managing one's illness gained through involvement with psychiatric rehabilitation practices and the recovery community. Many people with SMI talk about how they were isolated, lonely, and lacked a sense of purpose before becoming involved with a recovery community, which they often connected with through psychiatric rehabilitation.

When Should I Start Psychiatric Rehabilitation?

It is never too early (or too late) to begin a psychiatric rehabilitation program. People who are interested in pursuing work or school goals should look for opportunities to gain support for these goals. Clubhouses, drop-in centers, and organizations that provide peer support, such as *National Alliance or Mental Illness* (NAMI) or *Depression and Bipolar Support Alliance* (DBSA) can be wonderful places to form social relationships and connect to a community. Volunteer opportunities are plentiful in these spaces, so they can also be a good option to explore for people interested in volunteer work; in addition, they can lead to paid employment. Specialized psychiatric rehabilitation centers also provide opportunities to learn new things and because these often have connections to researchers who study cutting-edge approaches to rehabilitation, they might afford exciting new opportunities.

How Long Should I Be in Psychiatric Rehabilitation?

Some psychiatric rehabilitation options, such as clubhouses or supported employment/education, do not limit how long a person can receive these services. Thus, the decision of how long to remain involved has more to do with your preferences regarding whether the current involvement with the rehabilitation service has come to a natural end. For example, a focus on *supported education* might end or shift to a focus on supported employment once you complete a degree or certificate program. Some psychiatric rehabilitation programs have specified time frames. For example, someone may be involved in a course of cognitive remediation that lasts 6–9 months. The program ends once a skill has been learned and mastered.

How Do I Access Psychiatric Rehabilitation?

The types of services available differ dramatically depending on where you live; learning where to find these psychiatric rehabilitation services and how to access them can be challenging. Because the offerings are varied and not all providers are familiar with what is available, it is important to consult with other providers and families to identify options in your community. It can be helpful to find a provider who is knowledgeable about psychiatric rehabilitation options, and it can be useful to talk with your state's department of mental health and with leadership or members of organizations that serve other individuals and families in your area who face similar circumstances, such as local National Alliance for Mental Illness (NAMI) and Depression and Bipolar Support Alliance (DBSA) chapters. Some states also provide *outreach workers* or teams designed to provide direct support and assist individuals with navigating and connecting to psychiatric rehabilitation services in your area. Access to these outreach teams is often done through the psychiatric care providers or a state's department of mental health.

Because your goals and priorities often change, you and your family members and care providers should remain attuned to your rehabilitation needs over time. Just because you have refused a psychiatric rehabilitation option at one point in time does not mean that you will always refuse it. Look for opportunities to tour or schedule an informal, low-pressure, meeting with a staff person or service user at a psychiatric rehabilitation center. Family members or care providers can accompany you to these meetings. Another option is to help connect to a *peer specialist* who might be able to talk about these opportunities from their experience.

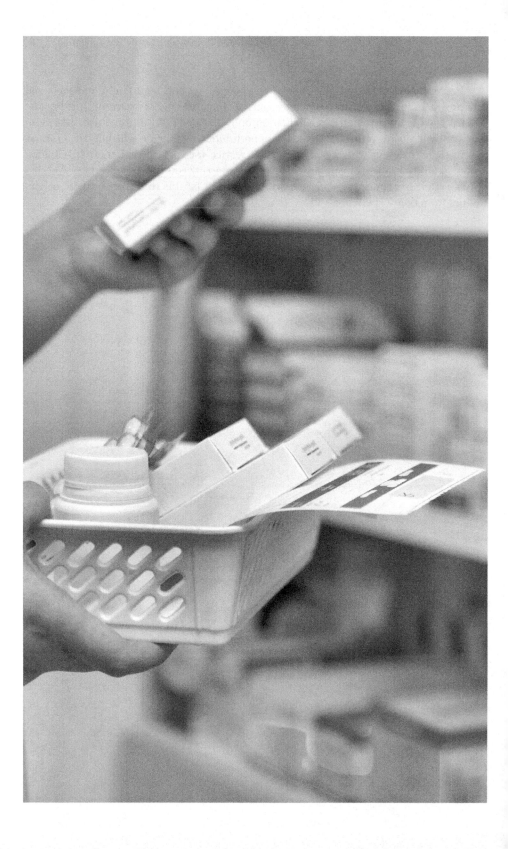

WHAT ARE MY OPTIONS IF I AM NOT GETTING BETTER?

Oliver Freudenreich, MD; Corinne Cather, PhD; and
Theodore A. Stern, MD

CHAPTER

In This Chapter

- Why Might My Symptoms Not Be Responding to Treatment?

- What Symptoms Are Unlikely to Benefit from Use of Psychiatric Medications?

- What Is Treatment-Resistant Schizophrenia?

- What Is Treatment-Resistant Depression?

- When Should I Switch Medications?

- Should I Combine Psychiatric Medications?

- Should I Consider Clozapine?

- Why Shouldn't I Use Clozapine As My First Treatment?

- What Are the Common Side Effects of Clozapine?

- How Long Will I Need to Take Clozapine?

- Should I Consider Electroconvulsive Therapy?

- Should I Try Herbs or Natural Medicines?

- What New Medications Might Be Available Soon?

- What New Approaches Are Being Investigated?

- Should I Participate in a Research Protocol?

Why Might My Symptoms Not Be Responding to Treatment?

Many people with *serious mental illness* (SMI) continue to have symptoms despite treatment. When this occurs, clinicians attempt to establish if *treatment-resistance* stems from *biological factors* or if treatment-resistance is due to factors unrelated to the illnesses' biology *("pseudo-refractoriness")*. It might be that medications are not being taken as prescribed. Medications are often effective for one aspect of a disorder *(target symptom)* and not for all manifestations of the disorder. *Antipsychotics*, for example, treat *acute psychosis* effectively and prevent *relapse* in *schizophrenia*. They are usually ineffective and can even exacerbate *negative symptoms* or *cognitive difficulties*. It would be an error to assume that treatment is not working if symptoms for which they are not intended to work are unaffected. Further, some people expect that a medicine will not work; this sets them up for a psychological resistance to a response, particularly if they were coerced into taking medication. Table 8-1 summarizes what clinicians consider when a person does not respond as expected to a prescribed treatment.

Table 8-1: Common Reasons for Non-Response to Psychiatric Treatment

"Pseudo-Refractoriness"
• *Diagnosis* incorrect
• Substance use that interferes with treatment*
• Insufficient dose of medication
• Insufficient duration of treatment
• Unusual genetic *metabolism* that requires higher dose
• Heavy cigarette smoking or other drug interactions that require a higher antipsychotic dose
• Insufficient medication adherence*

True Biological Non-Response
• Treatment-resistance to usually effective treatment
• Target symptom not responsive to selected intervention

*Most common reasons

The most common reasons for non-response to treatment is probably insufficient adherence. Often, medications are not taken for long enough (typically six weeks for an acute episode of psychosis) for them to work and treatment is mistakenly declared a failure. If medications are erroneously placed in the "didn't work" category, symptomatic people might be deprived of a potentially effective medication (and they might eventually run out of therapeutic options—there are only so many antipsychotics to try).

What Symptoms Are Unlikely to Benefit from Use of Psychiatric Medications?

You might not have any symptoms once your episode of psychiatric illness has resolved. While this improvement might take several weeks, this full restitution of health (*restitutio ad integrum* in Latin) is the goal of treatment for mood episodes in bipolar disorder and depression.

For other conditions, medications will only help with some, but not all, symptoms. In schizophrenia, antipsychotics are expected to work for *positive symptoms (psychosis)* but not for the negative or cognitive symptoms (such as apathy or *social withdrawal*). However, being free from positive symptoms allows you to participate in therapy and rehabilitation.

Many medications are effective for the core aspects of a *syndrome* (such as psychosis in schizophrenia). Problems with *motivation* or cognition are often not helped much by medications. In this case, the combination of medications and rehabilitation offers the best chance for recovery.

> ### ✻ Key Point
>
> Medication treatment by itself is rarely enough to resolve psychiatric symptoms. *Non-pharmacological* approaches (like psychological treatment and rehabilitation) are often as helpful as are medications.

What Is Treatment-Resistant Schizophrenia?

Some people have an excellent response to treatment while others have none. For most people, the response is somewhere in the middle. Roughly 20%–30% of people with schizophrenia fail to respond as expected to psychiatric treatment (Kane et al, 2019). Differences in response to treatment are expected; they reflect differences in our *genetic* make-up *(biological heterogeneity)*. Even though the symptoms that people experience might appear similar, their *physiology* might differ. In some areas of medicine, the biological reasons for these differences are understood, often at a molecular level (such as genetic differences in tumor biology), but for other conditions our understanding of the cause for symptoms remains a mystery. For many *acute* conditions like psychosis, a good response to medications can be observed in a matter of weeks. Quite often, improvement (such as sleeping better) is seen within a few days, while symptoms of psychosis might take longer to abate. If no response is seen after weeks, the chances for a good response to the treatment are slim, particularly in young people who are having their first-episode of psychosis (Emsley et al, 2006).

> ### ⅍ Key Point
>
> During an acute episode of psychiatric illness, improvement in symptoms can often be seen in a matter of days. However, rebuilding skills and relationships usually takes longer.

Treatment-resistance is often described in schizophrenia; however, it is on a continuum. Some people are "ultra-resistant," failing to respond to escalating treatments, including combination treatments. Others do not respond to second- or third-line treatments that usually work for treatment-resistance (such as *clozapine*). Since it is rare to not respond at all to treatment, the term *refractory* is no longer used. Instead, treatment-resistance, a relative term, is preferred. Quite often, treatment might not reduce core symptoms like psychosis, but it might improve associated symptoms, such as agitation or sleep problems.

In the future, studies will be conducted to identify biological subgroups of people who preferentially respond to each treatment. This strategy is already used for cancer care, where genetic profiles can determine if a treatment can work for your type of cancer.

Organizing care around varying degrees of treatment-resistance helps to organize care around the principle of *stepped care* (escalating treatment to the next level to avoid complacency). Table 8-2 summarizes the consensus definition for *treatment-resistant schizophrenia* (Howes et al, 2017).

Table 8-2: Consensus Diagnosis of Treatment-Resistant Schizophrenia (TRS)

Current Symptoms
• Symptom threshold at least moderate severity*
• Symptom duration at least 12 weeks
• Functional impairment at least moderate*
Adequate Treatment
• At least two trials of at least 6 weeks at a sufficient dose
• At least 80% adherence

*Established with a rating scale
Based on Treatment Response and Resistance in Psychosis (TRRIP) Working Group (Howes et al, 2017).

What Is Treatment-Resistant Depression?

As with schizophrenia, there are levels of resistance to antidepressant treatment (Fava, 2003). Unfortunately, some people with *treatment-resistant depression* (TRD) only receive selective serotonin re-uptake inhibitors (SSRIs), with switching from one agent to the next. When symptoms persist, *bipolar depression* should be considered for people with TRD because *lithium* or other *mood stabilizers* offer the best chances of improvement.

Of note: SSRI antidepressants are ineffective, at best, in bipolar depression (Baldessarini et al, 2020). If symptoms persist you should work with a psychiatrist who has experience in managing TRD so that potentially beneficial treatments can be considered and tried.

When Should I Switch Medications?

One of the more difficult decisions in the care of people with SMI is when to change treatment that is only partially effective. In many cases, a good-enough response coupled with tolerability might be better than a better response but with many uncomfortable side effects. In collaboration with your physician, you can determine which treatment is best; this is a *shared decision-making* paradigm. Commonly, non-medication approaches offer better chances for improvement than do adjustments in medications.

⚘ Key Point

Sequential trials (through trial-and-error) are needed to determine which medication represents the best compromise for you between efficacy and side effects.

If medications do not work well despite your best efforts, or if you are unable to tolerate them, you probably should switch treatments. It would be an error to continue medications that are largely ineffective. Treatment can often be increased, following an *algorithm* for treatment-resistance (stepped-care paradigm). For example, in schizophrenia, clozapine should be considered when treatment with *first-line antipsychotics* is ineffective.

Should I Combine Psychiatric Medications?

Combining medications (like combing *antihypertensive agents* to treat high blood pressure) is a common practice to enhance management. Similarly, in psychiatry, combining medications is often necessary to achieve a better overall response. For example, two mood stabilizers are often needed to control bipolar disorder. However, the benefit from combining antipsychotics is often questionable and should not be done routinely.

Persistent symptoms frequently respond to adding a more targeted medication. If a person with schizophrenia has sleep problems that have not abated with an antipsychotic, the judicious use of other medications for insomnia is reasonable.

One pejorative term for prescribing more than one psychiatric medication is *polypharmacy*. However, not all polypharmacy is the same (Freudenreich et al, 2012). Rational polypharmacy attempts to avoid duplication of effort (such as using two SSRIs) but combines medications that work by different mechanism (such as combining lithium with a second-generation antipsychotic). Medications used for different problems (for example, one for psychosis and one for insomnia) are similarly not examples of poor management. Sometimes one can use a medication that "kills two birds with one stone"—such as a sedating antipsychotic to treat psychosis and insomnia.

Combining antipsychotics or other add-on strategies to an antipsychotic, while common, is often not helpful (Correll et al, 2017; Hill and Freudenreich, 2013).

Combining different psychotropics can be considered when treatment is time-limited and when goals of treatment that can be measured. For some conditions, self-rating scales work well (depression, for example). Tracking symptoms over time helps in the assessment. For other conditions, one symptom might be the focus of attention.

⚘ Key Point

To avoid continually adding psychiatric medications, time-limited trials should be planned. After selecting target symptoms, a new medication can be added and continued only if there is clear benefit. Otherwise, the new agent should be stopped after a previously agreed-upon time interval (such as six to eight weeks for an antipsychotic). Medication discontinuation is as important (and often more difficult) as is starting a new medication.

Review of medications annually serves to determine the adequacy of current treatment, its safety, and whether all medications are still necessary.

Should I Consider Clozapine?

Use of clozapine deserves special mention, as it is the most effective antipsychotic that works even after usual first-line antipsychotics stop working (Hill and Freudenreich, 2013). Clozapine is the treatment of choice for treatment-resistant schizophrenia. It is also often used to manage thoughts of suicide in schizophrenia and sensitivity to *extrapyramidal symptoms* (EPS). It has a very low risk of causing *tardive dyskinesia* (TD).

Your doctor should recommend clozapine for you if you continue to have positive symptoms despite good adherence to another antipsychotic (Williams et al, 2017). For most people (80%), treatment-resistance appears at the beginning of treatment (with the first-episode of psychosis), although treatment-resistance can develop later on (Lally et al, 2016). Clozapine is also used for people with SMI who are chronically suicidal or aggressive.

Continuing to take an ineffective medication instead of trying clozapine is unwise; polypharmacy is often the result of treatment-resistance and it is associated with risks (for example, poorly-controlled symptoms, such as aggression and thoughts of suicide). In these instances, clozapine can be life-altering and even life-saving (Vermeulen et al, 2019).

⚘ Key Point

Don't deprive yourself of a chance for substantial improvement; consider using clozapine when other medications have not worked for your psychotic symptoms.

Why Shouldn't I Use Clozapine As My First Treatment?

Clozapine is not used as a first-line treatment because of its side effects and the need for regular blood monitoring. More importantly, most people with schizophrenia are not treatment-resistant and will do well with first-line antipsychotics that are easier to use and that cause fewer side effects. However, switching to clozapine should not be delayed for too long. All too often, clozapine is used after years of ineffective treatment with first-line antipsychotics and combination treatments, even though treatment-resistance is obvious. Current guidelines recommend that clozapine should be used after two adequate antipsychotic trials, preferably one with a long-acting injectable (LAI) antipsychotic (Howes et al, 2017). As a rule of thumb, if someone having their first-episode of psychosis does not improve after four to six months of treatment, clozapine should be the next step.

What Are the Common Side Effects of Clozapine?

When clozapine was developed, *agranulocytosis* (a dangerously low level of white blood *cells*) was found to be a major and potentially lethal side effect (Miller, 2000). It is rare (occurring in less than 1% of people), and mostly arises during the first 6 or 12 months of treatment. To recognize and manage this side effect, regular blood work is required. Additional side effects that are unique to clozapine include *myocarditis* and *sialorrhea*; others (such as seizures) are also more common compared to other antipsychotics. With close supervision, such symptoms can be managed.

Several long-term management problems from clozapine are sedation and weight gain (which can lead to risk of *metabolic syndrome* and *diabetes*).

How Long Will I Need to Take Clozapine?

A time-limited trial (such as three or four months) is usually long enough to determine if clozapine is better for you than other medications. Since it takes a while to titrate clozapine to a good dose, a clozapine trial is a bit longer than the customary six to eight weeks for an antipsychotic trial. Some people are unable to tolerate clozapine and will need to taper and discontinue it. Other people will continue to take clozapine despite the inconvenience of blood work because its benefits when compared to the benefits of other (ineffective) medications can be striking. After one year, the frequency of blood work that was initially done weekly (for six months) and then done every two weeks (for six months) decreases (to every four weeks). For most people, this frequency is acceptable given the clinical benefits of clozapine.

Should I Consider Electroconvulsive Therapy?

Electroconvulsive therapy (ECT) is a very effective treatment for many psychiatric disorders (including depression, mania, and psychosis) (Weiner and Reti, 2017). It is typically used as an acute treatment for mood disorders (such as severe depression) or when a quick response is needed (such as with *catatonia*). ECT is also used for *maintenance treatment* (such as monthly treatments) after the acute mood episode has resolved, but the commitment and possible cognitive side effects are significant. Therefore, it is generally reserved when use of a maintenance medication has proven ineffective.

While antipsychotics have supplanted ECT for the treatment of *psychotic disorders*, it is nevertheless effective and should be considered for people who show no response to antipsychotics, including clozapine (Lally et al, 2016).

Should I Try Herbs or Natural Medicines?

If a vitamin deficiency is diagnosed by established laboratory procedures, the deficiency should be treated. However, supplements are often added in the hope of making a difference or targeting some poorly defined deficiency, including a deficiency of trace elements. These investigations and treatments can be expensive.

Optimal management of SMI requires the use of medications that are approved by the *Food and Drug Administration* (FDA). The advantage of using FDA-approved medications is that they have been shown to work for your condition, and their safety has been tested. Also, you know exactly what medication you are getting and what dose is appropriate

With herbs or complementary medicines (also called natural medicines), none of those statements is necessarily true. They might not be effective, they might not be safe, and the pills bought over the internet might not even contain what they are said to contain. Just because something is labeled as "natural" does not make it safe. Any cursory googling of schizophrenia and supplements will generate a long list of compounds that could be tried, many of which will not have evidence of meaningful improvement of schizophrenia. It is far more likely to have little or no benefit than a convincing and impressive result. Some supplements may be too activating (such as energy drinks that contain caffeine or other stimulating substances) or be medically unsafe (such as muscle-building concoctions). Do not spend money on things that only offer marginal, if any, benefit—regardless of the "hype" that very small studies create—if there is a positive finding.

Unfortunately, most add-on strategies that have a good biological rationale have not provided evidence of clear benefits. All too often, results from small ("promising") trials have not been replicated by larger, well-conducted, trials. For example, the use of vitamin E for tardive dyskinesia is one example where early results could never be confirmed by later and more definitive trials (Soares-Weiser et al, 2018). There can even be unintended consequences. For example, in a lung cancer trial, the antioxidant vitamin E led to a worse outcome when added to cancer treatment—the exact opposite of the predicted effect.

If you want to take herbal medicines, discuss what you are taking with your doctor to make sure that there are no adverse drug interactions with your other medications. The best evidence might exist for *L-methyl folate* supplementation, for the negative symptoms of schizophrenia (Roffman et al, 2018) and to augment the effects of SSRIs in people with treatment-resistant depression (Goff, 2020; Papakostas et al, 2014). Drugs that boost the *N-methyl-d-aspartate* (NMDA) *receptor* might play a role in symptom management in schizophrenia (Javitt, 2006). *Sarcosine* or *glycine* are examples of supplements that can be purchased with this mechanism in mind. However, the best dose for them has not been established. *Omega-3 fatty acids* (which are very safe) were once hoped to delay or even prevent schizophrenia in young people who were thought to be at high risk for the disease—a hope that was dashed when a large trial failed to show benefit (McGorry et al, 2017). Vitamin D or B$_{12}$ are probably best reserved for instances where there is a diagnosed deficiency.

You should find a reputable source to make sure that the supplement you are buying contains the ingredient listed.

What New Medications Might Be Available Soon?

Drug development for a SMI like schizophrenia remains crucial for reasons: many patients achieve an insufficient response to available treatments (treatment-resistance); no treatment is available for core aspects of the disease (such as negative symptoms or cognition); and current treatments can cause medical side effects. Many antipsychotics, for example, cause weight gain and tardive dyskinesia. More broadly effective, better tolerated, and safer psychotropics are still needed. A clozapine-like antipsychotic for treatment-resistant schizophrenia, but without its side effects would be a welcome antipsychotic.

Current drug development focuses on developing new drugs that have different mechanisms of action. All available antipsychotics block *dopamine receptors*, which causes a range of side effects (increased *prolactin* levels, tardive dyskinesia, *parkinsonism*) in addition to their antipsychotic action. Non-dopaminergic antipsychotics might represent something truly new, with a better side effect profile, and perhaps even a better efficacy (Goff, 2020). New medications for cognition or negative symptoms would be an important breakthrough in the treatment of a variety of *neuropsychiatric disorders* where those two symptom clusters are affected. It might be unrealistic to find one drug that targets all aspect of complex neuropsychiatric disorders.

People often ask if they should try a new medication that was just approved by the FDA. New medications should be evaluated in the context of their efficacy and safety in comparison to current medications. Is the new medication truly more effective? Is it safer, particularly in the long run? New medications are expensive, and often their cost might not justify their benefit. Any medication change, despite its potential benefits, also risks relapse.

What New Approaches Are Being Investigated?

Increasingly, SMI is viewed as causing large-scale disruptions of *neural networks*. Targeting brain circuits directly (such as with *transcranial magnetic stimulation* [TMS]) is likely going to lead to new treatments soon, including those for management of symptoms (such as negative symptoms) where current medications are failing (Lindenmayer et al, 2019). However, such research will need to figure out how to "reset" the neural network.

More "thinking outside the box" has led researchers to study the gut *microbiome* as the gut's *microbiota* communicate with the brain (gut-brain axis) (Sandhu et al, 2017). Similarly, *anti-inflammatory* approaches are under intense investigation because inflammation seems to play a role in many aspects of brain function. Some approaches might become standard, such as use of *probiotics* (Ng et al, 2019) that target the microbiome or anti-inflammatory medications that target the immune system for psychiatric or neurological disorders (Miller and Goldsmith, 2017). However, at this point, it is difficult to identify which people might benefit from it. Given the potential risks, research is needed to identify subgroups that would benefit from the treatment.

ꙮ Key Point

Many seemingly breakthrough findings only have small or no effects. A key principle in medicine is "Do no harm." Harm can also be financial if money is spent on the promise of a cure. Most importantly, investigational treatments should not replace established treatments. Often, more effort should be invested in managing people with available treatments, as opposed to embarking on a quest for an elusive cure.

Should I Participate in a Research Protocol?

There is no progress without the participation of volunteers in *clinical research*. All available treatments are on the market because generations of patients have participated in clinical trials. For some people, participating makes them feel that they are contributing to science even if they do not benefit directly from the research study.

Sometimes, participating in a clinical trial provides benefits that would otherwise not be available, such as getting a new treatment. However, it is important to understand exactly what kind of research is conducted. Is it observational or is it interventional? Is it a medication trial or psychological research? Does it involve taking a medication that is already on the market or one that is new? Do I need to change my treatment or is the treatment just added on? Often, participants believe that they must benefit from participation in a trial. This is so common that it has a name: *therapeutic misconception*. In a trial with a *placebo* group, the group assigned to receive a placebo will not receive the investigational medication. Involving family members or a trusted friend can help decide whether you should enroll in a research study. Table 8-3 summarizes questions to ask when deciding whether to participate in a trial.

Table 8-3: Questions to Ask When Deciding About Participating in a Clinical Trial

What kind of trial is it?   • Is it observational or is it an intervention trial?
What kind of intervention is involved?   • What are its benefits and risks?
If it is a medication trial, do I need to change medications or are they added on?
Is there a placebo group?
What happens after the trial is over?   • Can I get the medication?
What is the time commitment?
How involved is it (will I need to complete imaging studies, blood work, rating scales)?
What do I get reimbursed for?

WHO AND WHAT ELSE CAN HELP ME?

Corinne Cather, PhD; Oliver Freudenreich, MD; and
Theodore A. Stern, MD

CHAPTER

What Can I Do to Help Myself?

You have already helped yourself by reading this book! Becoming educated about your illness and the best treatment options, which include medication (see Chapter 5), therapy (see Chapter 6), rehabilitation (see Chapter 7), and staying physically healthy (see Chapter 11), allows you to make informed decisions about how to manage your illness and your wellness. You might choose to read more about these topics; your health care providers will be more than happy to provide you with recommendations for resources that provide accurate and balanced information. Optimizing your treatment, including consistent use of medication, is key. Digital tools are increasingly available, and they can help you achieve optimal self-management.

Although taking medication is only part of the solution to obtain freedom from distressing symptoms, it is a critical component. You can get the most from your medications by taking them consistently and as prescribed. Although taking medications can be challenging, it helps to prevent relapse, so you should collaborate with your health care provider to create a regimen that you can tolerate and that is within the generally accepted therapeutic dose range.

⚘ Key Point

Treatment with medications might fail because it is taken at doses less than prescribed or less often than is prescribed. You should work with your health care provider to establish a medication regimen that you can commit to taking regularly and that your provider believes is at a therapeutic dose for you.

Many people with *serious mental illness* (SMI) have experienced negative consequences, such as hospitalization or interruptions in work, school, or relationships, after discontinuing their medications. Often, the issue of not taking medications (if the reason for missed medications is not having a system to remind you) as prescribed can be solved with the implementation of some simple strategies. In this case, you can set reminders on your phone or use a pill organizer and keep it in plain sight. Also, you should keep a day or two of back-up medications at other places you might sleep, such as your partner's or parents' house, and you should pair the timing of taking medications with an activity that you do every day (like charging your phone at night) or enlist the help of others. If you decide to discontinue or decrease your medications, it is better for you to be honest about this with your health care providers and members of your support system, rather than keeping this information to yourself. This allows more support to be put in place to mitigate the effects of any negative consequences.

> ### ❦ Key Point
>
> Implementation of several strategies can help you take medications more consistently. It is helpful to involve a family member and your health care providers in discussions about how you can make medications more accessible and consistently available, and it can help you identify and build in a "back-up system" for situations in which you are likely to miss medication doses.

One of the goals of therapy is to improve your capacity to manage your illness, which is referred to as "*illness self-management*" or "*self-management*." You can choose to augment therapy with self-help strategies (such as reading books or accessing online resources or digital applications). Many excellent books and free websites are available to help you learn more about mental health, some of which include the opportunity to freely consult with experts (such as https://smiadviser.org/), while others provide specific strategies to improve coping with symptoms of anxiety, depression, and anger, as well as other less commonly talked about symptoms, such as intrusive thoughts, hearing voices, suspiciousness, and *paranoia*. In recent years, there has been an explosion of digital resources designed to assist with goal-setting and accountability regarding general wellness goals (such as drinking more water, exercising, eating healthier, and being mindful of sleep hygiene) and ways to monitor the taking of medication. Also, there are many *mobile applications* that involve real-time interventions to target symptoms (Bell et al, 2018; Ben-Zeev et al, 2014).

> ### ❦ Key Point
>
> Smartphone apps can be a great way to augment other strategies you use to improve your illness self-management skills and general wellness. Check out several apps that aim to improve goal setting and accountability, track symptoms, enhance sleeping and eating, and provide coping strategies for bothersome symptoms.

Smartphone surveys and sensors (such as passive data collection tools that use location data) can provide valuable information about changing mental health symptoms and can personalize care plans (Torous and Keshavan, 2020). Although not yet available in most clinical settings, innovative *virtual therapies*, such as *avatar therapy* and *virtual reality-based exposure* paradigms hold promise for a wide range of symptoms, including phobias (Freeman et al, 2018), paranoia (Pot-Kolder et al, 2018), and hearing voices (Craig et al, 2018).

How Can My Family Help Me?

Just as you can help yourself by learning about your disorder and the optimal road to recovery, your family will be in a better position to help you if they become educated about your condition and what is available to help. Earlier in this book we discussed reasons why you might be hesitant to involve your family members in treatment; however, this might be of less concern when you learn that a large focus of including your family in treatment is educating them, so that they can be more helpful to you. If you have concerns about your family knowing about certain aspects of your treatment, you can provide a *limited release of medical information*, which limits your health care providers to sharing only the specific information that you want them to share.

⅍ Key Point

If you are wary of having your family members involved in your treatment, consider starting off by educating them, in general terms, about your illness and treatment. You have the option to provide a limited release of medical information, which restricts your provider to sharing only the information who want to have shared with your family.

Family members can be very helpful in supporting treatment recommendations and helping you follow through on work or school goals. For example, in Chapter 10, we reviewed *behavioral activation*, a strategy that helps both depressive and *negative symptoms*, (such as low *motivation* and expressivity). Health care providers can help you and your family members develop a mutually agreeable way for them to provide support (in a low-pressure way) and to plan and execute these activities. It is normal for people to have an easier time doing something with someone else than to do it alone. In terms of work or school, it often helps to have a family member sit next to you or help you compose an email, update your resume, or apply for a job. Your family can also use your support (called a mutual support strategy).

Staying consistent with medication-use can be facilitated by family members. Some people choose to share the date of their next medication refill with a family member, which can provide a back-up system to ensure there are no gaps in medication treatment caused by not having medication in your possession. Some health care providers will talk with you about having a family member observe your medication use, which is referred to as "*directly observed therapy* (DOT)." Direct observation might be indicated when a health care provider is trying to differentiate between a medication not working and it not working because you are having difficulties taking it consistently because of memory problems or other factors. Another indication for DOT is when a care provider is trying to help you avoid being hospitalized or having other adverse outcomes during an episode of worsening symptoms, and there is reason to believe that being more consistent with medication use will improve things.

> ### ⚘ Key Point
>
> Some health care providers will suggest that a family member directly observe you taking your medication (directly observed therapy), which can clarify how effective the medication is by taking *non-adherence* out of the equation (as it can be impossible to tell whether a medication is working if you don't remember taking it).

You can also enlist the help of a family member in the collaborative development of a *crisis plan*. Although crisis plans include steps to take in an emergency, the intent of a crisis plan is to avoid an emergency by identifying, planning for, and responding to *early warning signs* so that a crisis does not occur. (See Table 9-1 for an outline of a Wellness Recovery Action Plan [WRAP] that includes a crisis plan.) Early warning signs include subtle changes in emotions, thoughts, or behaviors that indicate a person is not doing well. Family members are often better at detecting early warning signs than are health care providers, which makes sense because they likely have more contact with you and have known you for your whole life. Ideally, you can identify at least one family member who can participate in this process. If possible, when you are well, crisis plans should be developed in collaboration with the supporters you have named in the plan because you want them to understand and agree to their roles before a crisis arises. It is a good idea for both you and the people named in your plan to keep a signed copy of the agreed-upon plan. However, unlike a *psychiatric advance directive*, this plan is not a legal document. If you are being treated under a section of the mental health law that governs involuntary care, people who support you might not be able to execute your wishes, depending on the specifics of the state law.

Table 9-1: Elements of a Wellness Recovery Action Plan (WRAP)

Wellness tools	What tools work for me? What new tools would I like to try?
	What gives me meaning, inspires me, and reminds me of my values?
	What should I avoid to stay well?
Daily *maintenance* of staying well	What do I need to do every day to keep myself feeling as well as possible?
	Which things do I need some reminding to do?
Trigger and early warning signs identification and action plan	What are my triggers?
	What can I do about these triggers?
	What are the signs that I am less well?
	What can I do in response to these signs to keep things from getting worse?

continued

Crisis plan	What are my signs of a crisis?
	Who do I want to be contacted in the event of a crisis?
	Who do I not want to have involved?
	Which treatments do I want?
	Which treatments do I not want?
Post crisis plan	What are my signs that I am no longer in crisis?
	What support do I need following a crisis?

Adapted from: Copeland M. Wellness Recovery Action Plan. *Occupational Therapy in Mental Health.* 2002; 17(3–4): 127–150.

> ### ❧ Key Point
>
> Crisis plans are not stand-alone documents about what to do in an emergency. Ideally, they are part of a wellness plan that emphasizes how to avoid a crisis. Crisis plans should be developed when you are well, in collaboration with the person or people you want to support you during a crisis.

How Can I Help My Family Cope with My Illness?

Your role might be to encourage your family members to seek help outside the family, noting that they can help you most when they help themselves. You might want to acknowledge that having a loved one with a psychiatric illness is stressful and forgive your family member for "nagging" you. Remember, most family members are simply trying to help—not to make your life more difficult. Whatever they do, it is likely their best attempts to solve a problem. Support can help family members deal with their emotional reactions to your illness; strike a balance in terms of their involvement in your treatment and your daily life; adjust over time, focus on their own life goals; engage in self-care; develop their relationships with family members other than you and with people outside of the family; and develop realistic expectations around your recovery. When family members receive support, feel hopeful, and appreciate what is reasonable to expect, they feel less stressed, and that can translate that into benefits to you. Some people have a family that holds stigmatized views about mental illness, psychiatric medication, and treatment. Only through connecting with other families (especially when they share a cultural background) can they accept that there is nothing shameful about mental illness and that treatment can make things better, not worse, for you and your family. The *National Association for Mental Illness* (NAMI) is an important organization that provides advocacy, as well as peer support, to family members and people dealing with SMIs. This advocacy and support are provided through a range of modalities, including telephone-based, online, and in-person care.

In addition to connecting your family to these supports, you should communicate openly with your family (and they should communicate with you) about what you need and expect from them in terms of their roles in your treatment and in terms of day-to-day interactions. Are their expectations of you too high or too low? Do you feel like you are getting too little or too much support from them? Episodically, you might consider including your family in sessions with your health care providers, which can go a long way toward keeping family relationships on an even keel.

How Can State Resources Benefit Me?

If you and your family members have become accustomed to the private system of care, you might be reluctant to avail yourself of resources offered through entities such as your state's *Department of Mental Health* (DMH), as it is called in Massachusetts. (The exact name varies by state.) However, the DMH offers several useful services that can be tailored to your needs and more intensive services (such as *case management*, housing, supported employment/education, and wrap-around treatment in the community, such as the *Program for Assertive Community Treatment* [PACT] teams) can be helpful in a time-limited way and can be used as a stepping stone toward increased independence. DMH case managers are mental health providers who serve as point people who coordinate care and check in with the client periodically to determine which services are being used, their satisfaction with these services, and their goals. Some DMHs offer supported employment/education to their clients directly (such as through PACT/ACT teams (described below) or other community outreach programs and clubhouses), whereas others outsource this to vendors who have connections to the DMH. PACT or *Assertive Community Treatment* (ACT) teams deserve special mention because they represent an *evidence-based practice* that provides team-based care to people in their homes and/or communities. ACT teams are multi-disciplinary, have low caseloads, and are designed to provide high-intensity and person-centered care (sometimes referred to as "a hospital without walls") to reduce future hospitalizations, legal involvement, victimization, and other adverse outcomes. Advocating for ACT-level services is strongly recommended if you or a family member has had several hospitalizations, is homeless or at risk for homelessness, or outpatient care is not working.

> ### ⚘ Key Point
>
> Assertive Community Treatment (ACT, or PACT) is an evidence-based, multi-disciplinary treatment delivered in the home or community to reduce hospitalizations and other negative outcomes for people with a history of numerous psychiatric hospitalizations.

The state can also help by applying for *entitlements* and other benefits, such as *Supplemental Security Income* (SSI) and *Social Security Disability Insurance* (SSDI); more information about deciding whether to apply for these is provided in Chapter 7. In some cases, if budgeting is a challenge for you, the state might assign a *representative payee* who manages your money and distributes it to you on a weekly basis so that you do not run out of money for food, rent, or other basic needs. When the legal system judges that you are unable to make decisions for yourself about medical or other life decisions, you might be assigned a legal *guardian* who acts as your representative. (See more about guardianship in Chapter 2.) Family members might need to retain private legal services for other financial or legal arrangements, such as *estate planning* and management of *discretionary trust funds*.

How Can I Get Help with Parenting?

People with SMIs have many important life roles (such as child, partner, sibling, and parent) and each of these roles deserves attention in terms of recovery goals while providing care for the whole person. The parenting role is one that is often overlooked in treatment, which is unfortunate because for many people, being a parent provides a deep sense of meaning. Moreover, parenting goals are among the strongest motivators of recovery. Some people who are diagnosed with a mental illness are concerned about whether they will pass their genetic risk for mental illness to their children. This concern can lead people to choose not to have children or to adopt; however, they might not be basing this on the available evidence of genetic risk. Genetic risk is based on information about your diagnosis, and family history of psychiatric diagnoses (and perhaps associated medical conditions), as well as your partner's psychiatric risk factors. If you are concerned about this risk, you and your partner should talk with your treatment team and possibly with a specialist in *genetics* about the best available estimates of genetic risk of illness transmission in your situation. Another common concern is the issue of balancing your recovery with the demands of parenting. By optimizing your recovery, you are also optimizing your readiness to face all of life's challenges and opportunities, including parenting. You can participate in parenting classes, read books on parenting, and prioritize parenting goals in individual and family therapy contexts that can help you with developmentally appropriate *disclosures* to your child about your mental illness. Other issues include managing parenting after a divorce and/or when there has been involvement by the *Department of Children and Families* (DCF) to protect the welfare of a child. (The agency's name differs from state to state.) These situations are difficult for anyone, but they offer added complexity when the parent with a SMI has had difficulties with parenting because of mental illness. Although challenging, it can be better to outline what needs to be accomplished to achieve your goals of reunification with the child and to enlist the help of DCF in meeting these goals, rather than entering into an adversarial relationship.

Should I Participate in Research or Try Other Treatments?

The decision of whether to participate in experimental research or to try a new treatment requires weighing the risks and benefits of choosing to participate (see Chapter 8 for more discussion of this issue). You should ask questions about the potential *direct benefits* of participating in the study, including whether the treatment is likely to have lasting positive effects once it is discontinued and whether it is available to you once the study is over. You should understand any possible short- and long-term risks of participation and learn about what help is available to you should adverse events occur. It can be helpful to know that all research studies are reviewed by *institutional review boards* (IRBs), which are designed to protect the rights and wellbeing of research participants in biomedical research. Also, important to know is that the decision to participate in research is always voluntary and can in no way compromise the clinical care that you receive now or in the future. For example, you cannot be told that you will be discharged from a clinic unless you participate in research. Also, you always have the right to discontinue your research participation at any time.

Should I Disclose My Psychiatric Illness to Others?

The decision of whether to tell others about your psychiatric diagnosis or your current and past treatment ("disclosure") is worth thinking about ahead of time so that you do not impulsively share information that you might regret later. This regret does not mean you are at fault for having a mental illness. However, many people do not know very much about mental illness and hold stigmatized attitudes about these conditions. Disclosure at work and school is discussed further in Chapter 7. However, another important question is how you will handle this disclosure with the people in your life at the time of your diagnosis and how you will handle this in the future. Disclosure usually does not have a "one-size-fits-all" solution. For example, what you decide to tell your closest friend is likely not going to be the same as someone you meet for the first time. Similarly, how you approach disclosure might change over time. You might become more comfortable talking openly about your past, or you might decide that the past is not very relevant because you have recovered. You might also want to consider the experience of the person you are telling about your mental illness. It can be more comfortable to talk with someone who has had mental health issues because he or she might be less likely to hold stigmatized views about mental illness. Unfortunately, stigma is a concern that is based in reality and that is fueled by ignorance or misconceptions about what it means to have had a diagnosis of schizophrenia or bipolar disorder or to have been hospitalized for thoughts of suicide or behaviors associated with depression. Given that most people in the general population do not understand what being diagnosed with a mental illness means and are likely to hold misconceptions, you should to refrain from using diagnostic labels when you decide to disclose. For example, it is probably not in your best interest to post on social media something like, "I was just diagnosed with bipolar disorder," or to call your roommates while you are psychiatrically hospitalized and say, "I have schizophrenia." We recommend starting slow with disclosure and telling only the people closest to you. You might start by describing your symptoms, rather than the diagnosis. For example, try saying, "My thinking was confused," "My thoughts were racing," "I was feeling very fearful, like others wanted to hurt me," or "I was having difficulty seeing the point of life." Some people are not comfortable sharing psychiatric information and choose instead to talk about it more generally; perhaps they might say that they have a medical problem that requires ongoing treatment. (Remember, people are likely to ask what type of medical problem, so you need to prepare for that.) Of course, what you decide to say and when you say it is completely up to you. You should feel empowered to control this information, including having conversations with your family and friends about information you would like them to keep private not share with others.

Sometimes, when a person is not well, he or she will have acted in ways that drew attention or perhaps disturbed or frightened people around them. If this happened to you, you might feel like you need to explain what happened. You might want to talk with a supportive person about how best to handle this. Sometimes, these things blow over, and people are no longer concerned. However, in some cases, it is worth trying to communicate that your behavior was caused by a psychiatric crisis that is now being treated. This is especially true if this behavior has caused you to feel guilty, ashamed, or bad about yourself. Sometimes, people with SMIs are afraid to consider dating or become romantically involved with another person because they are uncomfortable with the idea of disclosing their psychiatric histories. However, if the relationship progresses and you feel like it is important to tell your partner more about it, you can certainly choose how and when to do that. There is no rule that once you start dating someone, you need to tell them everything about your past. You might be surprised to find someone who understands mental illness because they have experienced it, either personally or with a family member. You might find someone who is open-minded and non-judgmental about your mental illness.

What Role Can Peer Support Play?

Everyone's experience is unique, including the experience with the same diagnosis, though people who have been through a SMI can often relate in ways that people who have had a SMI cannot. Peer support occurs when a person who has experienced mental health issues, trauma, and/or substance-use issues lends support to others with mental health challenges. Peer support might be offered on a volunteer basis, such as through NAMI's eight-week peer-to-peer program (https://www.nami.org/Support-Education/Mental-Health-Education/NAMI-Peer-to-Peer), another peer-run entity, or one embedded in systems of care. Many states provide specialized training in peer support that leads to a *certified peer specialist* (CPS) designation. CPSs and other peer support staff can be employed by the DMH (as it is called in Massachusetts) or human services agencies to model recovery and help others recover through sharing their own struggles and stories of hope. They can also work with clinicians, outreach counselors, and housing and employment specialists on enacting recovery goals.

A handful of large, well-designed studies of peer-facilitated recovery self-management interventions (such as WRAP, which was discussed earlier) have shown advantages over comparison conditions, particularly in terms of promoting self-perceived recovery and hopefulness (Cook et al, 2012a, 2012b, 2012c). One study also demonstrated that these interventions were associated with improved satisfaction with mental health services and a decrease in one-year hospitalization rates (Johnson et al, 2018). Although these studies are promising, more research is needed to identify both the mechanisms through which peer support has positive effects and to establish the efficacy of peer support services both within and outside of traditional mental health care settings (Gillard, 2019). Peer support is a growing occupation in the mental health care system today. However, the future of peer support as a part of traditional mental health care will depend, to a large extent, on the development of payment structures that are sustainable, as well as on dedicated efforts to integrate the sometimes-opposing philosophies of peer support and recovery principles of treatment. In other countries, community (mental) health workers are a prominent part of the health care workforce. They assume many of the roles that peer services bring to the table, but they are not people with lived experience. Many people find that connecting with peer support can be life changing insofar as peer supporters often serve as a bridge to a larger support network through recovery communities. Peer supporters work in diverse settings and can have many different titles depending upon their locations, organizations, and certifications. Peer supporters are sometimes called certified peer specialists, (CPS), *recovery coaches*, family partners, peer counselors, peer support specialists, *certified older adult peer specialists* (COAPS), *forensic peer specialists*, or peer mentors. There are a number of ways you can access peer support (see Table 9-2).

Table 9-2: How Can I Access Peer Support?

- Peer-run young adult access centers and advocacy networks
- Publicly-funded recovery centers (or recovery learning centers, as they are called in Massachusetts)
- Publicly-funded community-based mental health care service providers
- The Veteran's Administration System
- Inpatient and partial hospitalization programs
- Crisis stabilization units and respites
- Shelters
- Hospital emergency rooms
- "Warmlines"
- Mental health courts
- National Alliance for Mental Illness (NAMI) peer-to-peer program

HOW CAN I MANAGE MY EMOTIONS?

Corinne Cather, PhD; Oliver Freudenreich, MD; and
Theodore A. Stern, MD

CHAPTER

Why Is It Important for Me to Manage My Emotions?

Managing emotions effectively improves your quality of life, functioning, and overall happiness, while minimizing the adverse effect of negative emotions on your relationships, enhancing your productivity, and decreasing maladaptive behavioral patterns (such as self-harm or problematic use of drugs or alcohol). Negative emotions (such as sadness, worry, anger, and shame) are universal (see Table 10-1); they are part of what makes us human. However, not everyone manages or tolerates negative emotions equally well.

Table 10-1: Common Negative Emotions and Associated Thoughts, Feelings, and Behaviors

Emotion	Thoughts	Feelings	Behaviors
Sadness	"Nobody cares about me." "I'm not fun to be around."	Fatigue, low energy	• Oversleeping • Turning down invitations
Worry	"Something bad is going to happen to me or to someone I care about."	Chest tightness, shortness of breath, trembling/shaking	• Checking on the safety of family members and close friends. • Body scanning for uncomfortable physical sensations that might signify a health problem
Anger	"Other people are irresponsible and selfish."	Racing heart, tense muscles	• Aggressive driving • Yelling • Sarcasm
Paranoia	"People are out to hurt me."	Keyed up	• Hypervigilance to threat
Guilt	"I deserve to be punished."	Stomach upset	• Going back over things that you did in your mind that induce feelings of guilt
Shame	"I must have done something wrong that led to my being assaulted."	Chest tightness Stomach upset	• Avoiding close relationships

Individual differences in *distress intolerance* (defined as challenges in one's ability to tolerate negative emotions) might result from a combination of *biological factors* and life experiences; this distress intolerance is a risk factor for *psychological symptoms*. For example, some people experience negative emotions more intensely (higher *emotional reactivity*) because of a biological predisposition, which in turn, makes these emotions more difficult to deal with; this can lead to maladaptive responses (called *emotional dysregulation*). Others have had experiences that have taught them that negative emotions are bad (for example, being punished as a child for talking about negative feelings), which interfered with their ability to cope with unwanted emotions.

> ### ❅ Key Point
>
> Some people can have a biological vulnerability to experiencing negative emotions more intensely than others, which when combined with experiences that teach a person that negative emotions are something to avoid and to keep to oneself, can increase distress intolerance and emotional dysregulation.

To deal with negative emotions, some people engage in self-defeating coping strategies (for example, *social withdrawal* to the point of becoming *phobic*; use of alcohol and drugs; self-harm; or attempts at suicide). Fortunately, you can develop strategies to improve your ability to cope with negative emotions (that is, *distress tolerance skills*), derived from a type of therapy called *dialectical-behavioral therapy* (DBT), which is an overarching method of improving responses to emotions (see below). In addition, techniques have been developed to help with specific negative emotions (such as sadness, anxiety, and anger) that can be added to your coping repertoire to help you manage emotions more effectively.

What Are Some Common Problems in Emotion Management?

Problems with self-management of emotions occur for a variety of reasons, including, a lack of awareness about emotions, maladaptive responses to emotions (including trying to block out or avoid emotions, termed *emotional suppression*), and an underdeveloped toolbox of coping strategies. Another challenge to be faced is knowing when to work on managing your emotional response *(emotion-focused coping)*, when to work on solving a life problem *(problem-focused coping)*, and when to use a combination of strategies.

> ### ❅ Key Point
>
> Sometimes, strategies for emotional management are advisable, while at other times, problem-solving skills can ameliorate a difficult life circumstance; often, both skill sets can be employed.

Most people are aware when they are feeling "bad," but they have difficulty differentiating negative emotional states from one another ("Am I angry or sad?" "Am I guilty or ashamed?"). It is also common for people to misidentify a thought as a feeling, such as, "I feel as though I'm being taken advantage of" is a thought that can be associated with sadness, anger, or anxiety. Many theories of emotional management identify emotional awareness as a critical first step. Understanding the *thought-behavior-feeling model* of negative emotions is one way to help people become more adept at identifying what they are feeling. This model, which is central to *cognitive-behavioral therapy* (CBT), recognizes the tendency for certain emotions to be with linked with specific patterns of thoughts (and perhaps with mental images), behavior, and physical sensations (see Table 10-1). For example, sadness is often accompanied by thoughts of hopelessness ("This will never end"), worthlessness ("I am a failure"), and loss ("I will never regain my former self") and by feelings of fatigue or bodily heaviness. Learning how to recognize and label emotions is a critical to the selection of useful strategies for coping with emotions.

☘ Key Point

Learning how to identify and recognize emotions is a critical component of learning how to cope with emotions effectively. Understanding the links among thoughts, emotions, physical sensations, and behaviors can help you become more adept at identifying which emotion or emotions you are feeling. Conversely, blocking out emotions (emotional suppression) is generally considered counterproductive to effective emotion management.

One principle of emotional management is that suppressing negative emotions or engaging in behaviors to avoid awareness of negative feelings is, in general, counterproductive. However, you might find yourself using this approach. Through increasing your awareness of more effective methods to cope with negative feelings and by practicing these strategies, you can change the way that you respond to negative feelings.

What Is Motivation?

Motivation is the reason you choose to direct your energy toward a goal—for example, you might work for a paycheck *(extrinsic motivation)* or to feel proud of your accomplishments *(intrinsic motivation)*. When you hear the word, "goal," what often comes to mind are long-term goals, such as earning a degree or working in a field, However, everyday tasks, such as calling a friend, washing the dishes, and making your bed, can also be thought of as goals. One way that negative emotions interfere with functioning is by decreasing the *reward value* of a goal; conversely, more adaptive emotional management improves motivation and functioning. For example, if you are anxious, you might appear "unmotivated" to socialize because being in social situations is too distressing for you. Similarly, if you have depression, you might appear unmotivated to work because you often call in sick, in anticipation of not being able to complete your work or to tolerate feeling badly all day. Low motivation is a core component of the *negative symptoms* of *schizophrenia*. Although this label can be confusing, these symptoms are called "negative." These symptoms are not called negative because they are bad; they are called bad because they refer to things that are missing or diminished in people with schizophrenia. These symptoms include difficulty detecting emotions based on voice patterns, facial expression, or body movements/posture, as well as *emotional expressivity*, or a lack of motivation to socialize, work, or care for oneself (also known as *amotivation*). Although there are likely biological underpinnings for negative symptoms of schizophrenia, psychological factors play a role in the maintenance of low motivation and are promising targets of treatment. These factors include low expectations of pleasure or reward ("I won't have a good time"), low expectations of success ("I won't know what to say if I go"), and high expectations of the resources required ("It will be draining).

> **Key Point**
>
> The important point is that low motivation is often related to difficulty managing emotions. If you suffer from low motivation, neither you nor those close to you should misinterpret this as laziness or as some other character defect. A seemingly complete absence of motivation (amotivation) can represent a state of severe stress in which you have essentially given up trying that is due, in part, to chronic stress related to difficulties with emotional regulation.

How Can I Manage Feeling Sad?

Most people are aware that sadness, crying, feelings of worthlessness, and thoughts of suicide are *signs* of *depression*, but there are several signs of depression that might be less familiar, including, fatigue, difficulty with concentration, guilt, disturbances of sleep or appetite, irritability, or a heaviness in your body. Some people describe their inner feeling state as not having any feelings or "being numb or dead inside."

Depression is a syndrome in which many physical and psychological signs co-exist over several weeks and disrupt your functioning. Although those with a *diagnosis* of depression should be able to access an *evidence-based therapy* for depression, such as *Interpersonal Therapy* (IPT), CBT, *Problem-Solving Therapy*, or *Behavioral Activation* (BA), it is not always feasible to find a therapist skilled in these approaches. Therefore, you can seek to learn about key components of these treatments and to try to implement them in your life, perhaps in tandem with a self-help workbook (Greenberger and Padesky, 1995).

What Is Behavioral Activation?

Behavioral activation (BA) refers to the gradual increase of planning and participating in activities designed to promote productivity and enjoyment. The rationale for this intervention is that depression tends to lead to reduced levels of activity and is thought to be maintained by this decrease because activities that promote self-worth and enjoyment help to maintain positive mood states. A general treatment principle is to "act in opposition;" this means that you should work to overcome your natural tendencies to respond to symptoms and do the opposite of what you are inclined to do or what you have done in response to negative mood states. Commonly, those with depression turn down invitations from others for social engagements, spend more time sleeping, and engage in sedentary activities; this disengagement depletes your energy and your ability to enjoy life. A starting point for behavioral activation is to record your weekly activities on an activity schedule and rate each one (on a 0–10 scale in terms of the degree of enjoyment and feeling of accomplishment you derived from that activity; see Table 10-2). Additional activities are gradually increased over time, and as a result, you do more over time. Sometimes, while doing this work, you may become aware that you are getting more out of activities than you had predicted, which can help you overcome negative expectations that were maintaining your depression. With BA, weekly mood ratings are assessed so that you can evaluate how well this is working. Advantages of BA are that it is brief (lasting approximately six weeks), relatively straightforward, and has been as effective as CBT for depression (Ekers et al, 2014). BA is also a promising approach for overcoming negative symptoms and motivational deficits.

Table 10-2: Example of Weekly Schedule Used to Promote Behavioral Activation and Track Enjoyment (E) and Productivity (P) on a Scale of 0 = None to 10 = Highest Possible

	Mon	Tues	Wed	Thurs	Fri	Sat	Sun
8–10	Shower (E = 4, P = 5)			Shower (E = 4, P = 9)		Shower (E = 5, P = 7)	—
10–12	Lie in bed (E = 4, P = 2)	Walk around block (E = 5, P = 6)			Doctor appt (E = 5, P = 5)		Laundry (E = 2, P = 9)
12–2	Lunch at home (E = 4, P = 2)			Therapy appt (E = 3, P = 6)			Lunch at sister's (E = 9, P = 7)
2–4	TV (E = 3, P = 0)	TV (E = 4, P = 3)	TV (E = 3, P = 0)	Coffee Shop (E = 7, P = 5)	TV (E = 3, P = 0)		
4–6			Water plants @ Mom's (E = 7, P = 9)			Pharmacy to pick up meds (E = 4, P = 8)	Visit the park (E = 9, P = 5)
6–8	Dinner at home (E = 6, P = 3)					Dinner at restaurant w/parents (E = 3, P = 5)	
8–10	TV (E = 7, P = 3)						
10–12	Bedtime	Bedtime	Bedtime	Bedtime	Bedtime	Bedtime	

> ### ✣ Key Point
>
> Purposefully scheduling progressively more activities that are designed to increase your enjoyment and sense of accomplishment improves mood. This technique produces results that are like those of longer courses of CBT and thus, can be effective for the self-management of depressive symptoms.

What Are Other Coping Skills for Depression and Guilt?

CBT for depression incorporates BA and uses a technique called *cognitive re-structuring*, which refers to the identification and modification of surface-level beliefs (negative *automatic thoughts*, such as "I'm not going to do a good job at work today") and more deeply held beliefs about yourself or the world (*core beliefs*, such as "I'm a failure") that are characteristic of depression. One of the first steps in CBT is to learn about the thought-behavior-feeling model of depression and how to use self-monitoring (a method of recording situations, as well as associated thoughts and feelings), when experiencing a downturn in mood to learn how this approach applies to your situation. CBT also teaches about thinking biases that operate to make these beliefs resistant to contradictory evidence. For example, the *magnification bias* refers to the tendency to magnify mistakes and minimize successes. CBT for depression helps people learn how to identify thinking that is subserved by these biases and methods to challenge these thoughts to arrive at more a balanced view of yourself, others, and the world that can also be helpful for managing disproportionate guilt. Dr. Judith Beck, in her classic book about CBT for depression, described an exercise in which people work with a therapist to alleviate guilty feelings by arriving at more balanced views regarding the proportion of the negative event that they bear responsibility for and the proportion of the responsibility that is attributable to others or to external factors that were beyond anyone's control (Beck, 2021). There are many excellent self-help workbooks and online resources available to help people with depression.

How Can I Manage Thoughts of Suicide or Suicidal Behavior?

Suicide and *non-suicidal self-injury* (such as cutting or burning oneself) can be understood as an attempt to escape (avoid) the experience of overwhelming negative emotions. People who develop the wish to die often perceive themselves as alone in the world and at the same time, a burden to others (Joiner, 2005), which, in combination with impaired problem-solving associated with emotional dysregulation, leads a person to erroneously conclude that suicide is the only solution. DBT, a type of therapy that represents an evolution of CBT, was developed specifically to target suicidal thoughts and behavior through the development of *present-centeredness*, emotion regulation (distress tolerance) skills, and skills to promote *interpersonal effectiveness* and improve relationships. Therapy techniques include the development of a coping plan for suicidal impulses, identification and modification of thoughts that trigger suicidal impulses, problem-solving to increase cognitive flexibility so that suicide is not the only apparent solution, and increased salience of reasons for living including developing a *"Hope Kit"* (a personally meaningful collection of objects) (Wenzel and Jager-Hyman, 2012).

How Can I Manage Excessive Worry?

Anxiety disorders include *generalized anxiety disorder* (GAD), *panic disorder* (with or without *agoraphobia*), and *social anxiety*. *Obsessive-compulsive disorder* (OCD), is also common, but it has been re-conceptualized in newest version of the Diagnostic and Statistical Manual-Fifth Edition (DSM-5) as a spectrum of related disorders. Anxiety disorders tend to co-occur with other anxiety disorders (they are highly co-morbid) and to co-occur with depression, and with substance use disorders. At the core of anxiety disorders are *cognitive biases* and *avoidance* behaviors. Common cognitive biases include overestimating the probability of negative outcomes and catastrophizing about the severity of those negative outcomes. People with significant anxiety tend to avoid environmental situations or internal states that trigger anxiety. For example, someone with social anxiety might avoid delivering talks to others (environmental) and a person with panic disorder might avoid becoming overheated or exercising vigorously because they choose to avoid certain physical sensations, such as sweating or a racing heart (internal), which trigger concerns that they could be having a catastrophic medical event, such as a *heart attack*. Another more subtle form of avoidance is the use of *safety behaviors*—these are actions taken to avoid, prevent, or manage a potential threat, such as always carrying anxiety medication, checking on others' safety to manage worry, researching the location of hospitals while travelling, or always sitting near the door in a movie theater should they need to leave suddenly.

Key strategies to help people manage anxiety include decreasing avoidance and increasing exposure to feared stimuli, using strategies to contain worry, and engaging in relaxation/mindfulness practices. Exposure can take several forms, including, doing things that have been avoided, purposefully inducing physical symptoms that a person is afraid of (to improve tolerance of these experiences and to show that the feared consequence does not occur, or imaginal exposure to a feared event using a script or audio-recording that is played over and over again). A common analogy for the rationale for exposure is to think of what it would be like to watch a scary movie over and over again—the first time, the person is likely to react strongly, but once a person learns what is in the movie and what will occur, the scary scenes are unlikely to provoke fear and can even begin to appear funny. Creative treatment strategies can induce physiological symptoms that mimic feared sensations to treat panic disorder (interoceptive disorder), for example, breathing through a straw to induce shortness of breath, or pressing lightly on one's throat to create a sensation of throat tightness or choking. When it is difficult to arrange situational exposures (such as giving a presentation at work) sometimes it is helpful to enlist the help of *confederates*, or people who act as though they are audience members for a presentation, so that you can work on exposing yourself to this fear.

One worry management strategy that is unfamiliar to many is *worry scheduling*. In worry scheduling, you schedule time during day where for 45 minutes, you actively spend time worrying; this means that when worries occur at other times of day, you will not engage in worrying. You are instructed to keep a list of worries that occur during the day and then, at the specified time of day, you can write about these worries during the "worry time," after which you are instructed to practice a relaxation technique for 10 minutes. For many people, this strategy results in less time spent worrying and it increases the sense of control that they have over their worrying.

There are many forms of *relaxation training* to help with worry; these include *breathing re-training, progressive muscle relaxation, yoga,* and *mindfulness-based strategies.* One of the common mistakes that people make is not thinking about this as a practice—to use these strategies effectively when you are worrying, you should practice these strategies daily, ideally not when you are not worried. As a result of this practice or training, you can decrease your baseline level of anxiety and get quick results in emergency settings when you are worried. Another variant of mindfulness training is *attention re-training*—this is when you focus your attention on everyday tasks, such as washing dishes or taking a walk, to disrupt the worry sequence and increase your experience with thoughts that are not about worry.

How Can I Manage Problematic Anger?

People who seek anger management strategies have often been told by others that their anger is problematic because it has resulted in altercations, inappropriate actions, or dangerous behavior. Although people with anger issues often perceive that their anger escalates out of the blue to a breaking point, usually people can learn to identify their *early warning signs* of anger. These can be physical signs, such as muscle tension or a racing heart, or behaviors, like driving quickly, talking loudly, or cursing. Identifying early warning signs is important because the most common problem with anger is that people react without thinking through the consequences; therefore, identifying anger in its early stages permits the person to slow down, consider what is making him or her angry, and decide what to do about it. Often, it is helpful for the person to remove themselves from the situation or to distract themselves before deciding how to respond. Although this might sound like emotional suppression, it is not. It is meant to disconnect the anger from the problematic response. Road rage is a good example of this. If another driver cuts you off, there is not much you can do about it. Getting heated up, cursing, and yelling at them, racing after them and trying to cut them off carries risks to the person and does not solve anything. Instead, it might be better to pull off the road, get a cup of coffee, return to the car, and listen to music and congratulate yourself for handling your anger well and not "taking the bait" and getting heated up. Another revelation for people who have difficulty managing their anger can be learning the difference between aggressive and assertive responding. Through experience, people can learn that expressing themselves assertively in interpersonal situations can lead to better results than will expressing themselves aggressively (see Table 10-3, for a description of this skill).

Table 10-3: Communication Skills to Promote Interpersonal Effectiveness and Get What You Want

		What to Do	Examples
D	Describe	Be clear and specific.	"Please put away the laundry I folded."
E	Express	Say how you feel.	"I feel unappreciated when you put clean laundry back into the hamper."
A	Assert	Get to the point—avoid indirect communication.	"I am only able to do one load of laundry a week, so please keep it to one full hamper."
R	Reinforce	Provide rewards and reinforcement when your communication results in the desired outcome.	"Thank you."
M	Mindful	Stay focused on the goal of the interaction.	Don't get distracted by other issues.
A	Assertive	Project confidence.	Pay attention to your posture, eye contact.
N	Negotiate	Be open to compromise.	It's rare to get everything we want all the time.

Adapted from: Linehan M: *DBT Skills Training Handouts and Worksheets.* New York: The Guilford Press. 2015.

How Can I Manage Shame or Intrusive Memories of Trauma?

Trauma can produce a host of negative feelings and sometimes it is necessary to address the traumatic experience more directly for a person to move forward and live their life fully again. This is especially true when a person suffers *post-traumatic stress disorder* (PTSD), which can be present when a person continues to feel as if the traumatic experience was happening to them (such as through nightmares or flashbacks), avoidance of reminders of the event, constantly being "on guard" or keyed up, and these experiences affect their ability to function. Two forms of therapy have been helpful for overcoming PTSD—these are *exposure therapy* and *cognitive processing therapy* (CPT). Both of these treatments involve some degree of going over the event—remember, consistent with the idea that avoidance of thinking about negative emotion or emotional suppression is bad, this involves the opposite, or considering one's emotional reactions and experiences leading up to, during, and after the event by coming back in contact with them—either through telling someone about it or through writing. Although it is difficult to bring this into one's awareness, and by repeated telling of one's story, it becomes easier. Because the experience is difficult, doing this with a therapist is usually a good idea. Through CPT, distorted beliefs (such as "It was my fault that this happened" or "I am a damaged person who can never have healthy relationships again") can be identified as keeping a person stuck in the experience of PTSD symptoms and preventing them from moving forward with their lives. By learning how traumatic experiences affect people and helping them modify these beliefs, people can move forward.

How Can I Change My Alcohol and Drug Use?

If you are aware that you are using substances to manage negative feelings, you are already taking steps along the path of figuring out alternative ways of coping with negative feelings because one of the first steps to addressing alcohol or drug use is to answer the question, "What am I getting out of using alcohol or drugs?" People use alcohol or drugs for a variety of reasons, including the enhancement of positive feelings; because they have become part of a routine; because they have become dependent on them (meaning they experience *withdrawal* symptoms when they stop using them); or because they are a way of coping with negative feelings. Typically, using substances to cope with negative feelings is not very effective and likely falls under emotional suppression, which often creates more problems than it solves. Once a person has a greater understanding of the reasons that they use substances, there can be some benefit in terms of facing an emotion they have been avoiding. The other side of this strategy is identifying some of the problems with using alcohol or drugs and learning how the use of alcohol and drugs is causing the person problems now and how it could cause longer-term problems or difficulties. Sometimes, your family members and close friends can identify problems that you can't recognize. This exercise is often referred to as a decision matrix or pro/con matrix (see Table 10-4) and it can be one of the first steps in deciding whether to address the substance use.

Another potential strategy includes replacing the function of the substances. For example, if alcohol or drugs was a way for you to get more enjoyment out of life, think of other ways to make life more enjoyable. If these substances helped you cope with anxiety in social situations, try to tackle the social anxiety using other means. Because it is common to use substances in social situations and because other people might have become accustomed to you using substances, you might also need to develop ways of saying "no" to using alcohol or drugs (in other words, *refusal skills*). You might also want to gear your socializing to activities in which alcohol or drugs are less likely to be used—for example, outdoor activities, such as hiking, biking, or walking; getting coffee with a friend; or going to the movies. You might also want to develop a social network that does not use alcohol or drugs often or at all (such as *sober social network*). To find the latter, you might want to connect with local chapters of *alcoholics anonymous* (AA) or *Self-Management and Recovery Training (SMART Recovery)* in your area.

If you think you might be dependent on a substance, such as alcohol or *opiates*, it is important for you to know that there might be medications available to help you reduce or stop using these substances. Some of these medications are available as a monthly injection (such as *Vivitrol®* and *Suboxone®*) and are quite effective in reducing *craving*. Talk with your doctor about whether medication-assisted treatment might be appropriate for you.

Table 10-4: Example of a Pro/Con Decision Matrix

Behavior	Drinking Six Beers Per Night	Drinking Three Beers Per Night
Pros (good things/ advantages)	• Relaxing • Makes it more fun to listen to music and watch movies • Reward myself after work • Passes the time • Helps me fall asleep	• Might lose some weight • Might focus more on eating a better dinner • Spend less money on beer • Easier time waking up in the morning • More clear-headed next day
Cons (bad things/ disadvantages)	• Hard to get up in the morning • Might be bad for my health longer term • A lot of calories • Expensive • Might be missing out on dating opportunities by staying home and drinking • My mom nags me about drinking	• I would want to have more • I might have trouble falling asleep • Would not be as much fun as drinking six beers

Instructions: Identify a current behavior you want to evaluate and a possible alternative behavior that you can picture yourself doing instead of the current behavior. Write down the pros (good things or advantages) and cons (bad things or disadvantages) of each behavior. Consider both the long-term (next 1–5 years) and short-term (next 3–5 days) pros and cons of each behavior.
Behavior I am currently doing that I want to evaluate: Drinking six beers per night.
Alternative possible behavior: Drinking three beers per night.

What Is Positive Psychology?

A sea change in psychology is the *positive psychology* movement, which shifted the focus from exclusively eliminating negative mood states to what would need to be done to build more positive mood states. This work has generated a wealth of techniques designed to build upon a person's strengths and bolster positive patterns of thought and behavior. One example of this exercise is the "Three Good Things" exercise, which tasks a person with reviewing his or her day to reflect on three positive things that happened that day (in contrast with what would occur in a negative mood state). The person then links one of the positive things to a specific positive quality that he or she believes to be true about him or herself (Seligman et al, 2005). Other interventions along these lines include positive mindfulness and *self-compassion* exercises, which decrease depression, possibly thorough increased awareness of the present and decreased judgmental responses to themselves and others (Schuling et al, 2020).

What About Exercise?

Exercise holds promise for reducing depression symptoms (see Chapter 11). Adding moderate exercise to CBT appears to improve the efficacy of CBT for people with moderate depression, with stronger effects for older people (Borbeau et al, 2020). Even low-intensity exercise decreases depression among people in the general population (Hu et al, 2020). Results of exercise on reducing anxiety symptoms are more mixed (Borbeau et al, 2020; Stonerock et al, 2015); however, exercise has strong effects on *anxiety sensitivity* (the extent to which a person is fearful of bodily sensations associated with physiological arousal). Anxiety sensitivity is one of the cross-cutting dimensions thought to play a role in the development of psychiatric disorders, suggesting that it might hold trans-diagnostic promise (Jacquart et al, 2019).

HOW CAN I BECOME AND STAY HEALTHY?

Corinne Cather, PhD; Oliver Freudenreich, MD; and
Theodore A. Stern, MD

CHAPTER

In This Chapter

- Why Is It important to Pay Attention to My Physical Health?

- What Are Common Health Problems for People with Serious Mental Illness?

- Why Do People with Serious Mental Illness Have More Health Problems?

- Why Isn't Smoking Cessation Addressed Optimally?

- Why Isn't Diabetes Addressed Optimally?

- How Do I Decide Which of My Health Problems to Address First?

- How Can I Get Help for Smoking Cessation?

- What Can I Do to Try to Eat Healthier?

- What Can I Do to Be More Active?

- How Can I Improve My Sleep?

- Which Preventative Health Appointments Should I Keep Up with?

- How Can My Primary Care Doctor or Psychiatrist Help Me?

- What Is a Health Care Proxy and How Do I Put This in Place?

- How Can My Family or Others Close to Me Help?

Why Is It important to Pay Attention to My Physical Health?

Many chapters in this book address the psychological aspects of having a *serious mental illness* (SMI). This is important because recovery requires attention to psychiatric symptoms, role functioning, and personally meaningful goals (see Chapter 12). However, recovery can only occur if you are physically healthy enough to work on these other areas. For example, you might recover psychologically from a SMI, yet die from a *heart attack* triggered by years of cigarette smoking and from neglect of your physical health. On average, people with a SMI die decades earlier than do those without SMIs, largely because of medical causes (and not suicide). A frequent cause of early death in those with a SMI is *heart disease*, so it is crucial to focus on factors that contribute to heart disease (cigarette smoking, *diabetes,* an unhealthy diet, and a sedentary lifestyle).

> **Key Point**
>
> Living well with a SMI requires as much attention to your physical health as you must give to your psychological wellbeing. There is no mental health without physical health (and vice versa).

What Are Common Health Problems for People with Serious Mental Illness?

Smoking, diabetes, and *obesity* are each more common among people with SMI than in those in the general population (Dickerson et al, 2013; Osborn et al, 2008). Moreover, people with SMI are more likely to have poorer diets and to be more sedentary than are those without mental health problems (Teasdale et al, 2019). This is not to say that people with SMI are to blame for their health problems because some factors are outside of their control. However, you should be aware of what you can do to become and stay healthy, particularly with regard to the most common cause of death—heart disease and its *risk factors.*

People with SMI smoke cigarettes at rates that are two to three times higher than in those who don't have a SMI. For example, nearly two-thirds (62%) of people with schizophrenia and roughly one-third (37%) of people with *bipolar disorder* smoke cigarettes, compared to 17% of those who don't have either of these SMIs (Dickerson et al, 2018). Sadly, the life expectancy of people with SMI, such as schizophrenia, is reduced by 20 years or more; this decrease in life expectancy is largely caused by *cardiovascular* and *respiratory diseases* related to smoking (Cook et al, 2014; Olfson et al, 2015). The lifetime rate of diabetes among people with a SMI is 15%, which is approximately twice the rate seen in the general population (Osborn et al, 2008). Suboptimal diabetes management in people with a SMI is common and contributes to more diabetes-associated problems (Frayne et al, 2008). Further, people with mental health problems are more likely to be overweight or obese than those who don't have a SMI and who have less-healthy dietary habits. People with mental health conditions consume more calories, salt, sweetened drinks, and caffeine than do those without mental health conditions and they are less likely to eat fruits, vegetables, fish, nuts, and vegetable oil compared to people without mental health conditions (Teasdale et al, 2019). *Sedentary behavior* (as measured by GPS data from cell phones that reveals how far and how often a person moves or changes locations) is also much more common among people with a SMI, and it might be a marker of low *motivation* (Depp et al, 2019).

Why Do People with Serious Mental Illness Have More Health Problems?

Medicine and society are becoming more aware of how social factors, for example, the neighborhood in which a person lives or their social support, contribute to the *incidence* and *prognosis* of disease (Marmot et al, 2008). In addition, recent work on *health inequities* from the uneven delivery of care to people with certain demographic factors, reveals that rates of cigarette smoking have not been declining among people with SMI as much as they have among people in the general population, suggesting that effective treatments for smoking cessation are not reaching those with SMI (Cook et al, 2014).

There are a variety of reasons why a person with SMI remains at higher risk for these conditions and why, once they have these conditions, that they are at higher risk for worse outcomes. These explanations include patient-related factors (such as *symptoms*, knowledge about health, and the level of engagement in health-promotion behaviors); health-care related factors (such as lack of access to care and suboptimal care); physician-related factors (such as low expectations and knowledge deficits about optimal treatment); and family-related factors (such as family norms about health behaviors and stressors that interfere with the ability to provide support for better health for those with SMIs).

Why Isn't Smoking Cessation Addressed Optimally?

Obstacles to smoking cessation include attitudes or myths held by health care providers and family members, including the pernicious, incorrect idea that people with SMI cannot or do not want to quit smoking; they need to smoke for psychological benefits; or that smoking cessation medications will not help and may exacerbate psychiatric symptoms (Prochaska, 2011). Over the last decade, there was a concern that state hospitals would be overwhelmed by waves of violence if psychiatric hospitals became smoke-free institutions. Suffice it to say, this never materialized, and psychiatric hospitals today are smoke-free. In fact, psychiatric practitioners probably contributed to the problem by organizing programs around smoke breaks, rather than prioritizing offers to help with smoking cessation.

Additional factors put forth to explain the high rates of smoking in people with SMI—particularly in people with schizophrenia—include smoking as a coping strategy for symptoms, side effects of medication, or cognitive impairment. Unfortunately, *antipsychotic treatment* contributes to weight gain (and perhaps to diabetes). People with SMI might also be less aware of the health risks associated with smoking and diabetes than those who don't have a SMI. Also, people with SMI might be less knowledgeable about how to manage those health risks.

Historically, smoking-cessation medications have been underused in this population, even though they are safe and effective. It's possible that smoking-cessation medications are under-prescribed to people with schizophrenia due to ongoing concerns over their safety of combining them with psychotropic medications, low expectations regarding patient follow-through or success with quit attempts, or simply a lack of practitioner knowledge about efficacy of these medications. This reluctance to recommend and prescribe effective smoking-cessation therapies likely contributes substantially to the disparity in the rates of successful smoking cessation among people with schizophrenia.

Why Isn't Diabetes Addressed Optimally?

Unfortunately, only about one-third of people with SMI are screened for diabetes (Mangurian et al, 2016), and among those diagnosed with diabetes, people with mental illness are less frequently monitored for glycemic control and cardiovascular risk factors than those who don't have a SMI (Osborn et al, 2008). (See Chapter 5 for recommendations about how often this testing should be completed for people taking *antipsychotic* medications.) Suboptimal care might be improved by newer models of care, such as *behavioral health homes* and *accountable care organizations* (ACOs), which facilitate the integration of psychiatric and medical services.

Also, people with a SMI have less knowledge about their diet and they report more difficulty obtaining and/or cooking food. These differences might be driven by living conditions and less-healthy food options (such as residential programs), limited knowledge about a healthy diet, life stress, hunger due to medications or boredom, or preference for fast foods that are high in sugar, salt, and fat and that are lower in nutrients. In combination with a reduction in regular exercise, these challenges to healthy eating could explain physical health problems and early mortality for people with mental health problems.

How Do I Decide Which of My Health Problems to Address First?

The answer depends on several things, including, which health problem you want to address first, the advice of your health care providers, and knowledge about the risks and benefits associated with treating (or not treating) different health behaviors or conditions. If you are a smoker, health care providers often say that the single best thing you can do for your health is to quit smoking. First, half of all smokers will die from a smoking-related illness. Second, the benefits of smoking cessation are dramatic for all age groups (see Table 11-1 for benefits of smoking cessation for different age group). Third, the risks of smoking are equivalent to those of being approximately 100 pounds overweight, so unless a person is 100 pounds or more overweight, there are more health risks associated with smoking than with being obese. Fourth, light smoking (smoking only a few cigarettes each day) or intermittent smoking carries substantial health risks. There is no safe amount of smoking (Schane et al, 2010). However, you should weigh this information, review the steps below to address various health issues, and make a decision about what makes the most sense for you in terms of where to start.

Table 11-1: Benefits of Quitting Smoking by Age Group

Age Quitting in Years	Years of Life Gained
25–34	10
35–44	9
45–53	6
55–64	4

Note: Every cigarette takes an average of 9 minutes from your life expectancy (Jha et al, 2013).

☘ Key Point

Choose wisely which problem you address first and which you can delay. Some problems might not feel urgent until it is too late (such as postponing weight loss to lower your blood pressure until you have a heart attack or stroke). Quitting cigarette smoking *now* might offer you the "biggest bang for the buck," and it should be at the top of every smoker's list—even if you do not feel that it is urgent now.

How Can I Get Help for Smoking Cessation?

Recently, the *EAGLES trial* was conducted with smokers with and without mental illness who wanted to stop smoking (Anthenelli et al, 2016). Participants in this trial (more than 8,000 people) were provided with one of the three medication treatments for smoking cessation: *varenicline (Chantix®)*, *transdermal nicotine patch* (the *nicotine patch*), *bupropion* (Wellbutrin®/Zyban®), or a *placebo* for 12 weeks. Neither the participants nor the experimenters knew which treatment each person received. Everyone also received weekly, brief *behavioral counseling* for smoking cessation. The results of this study showed that smokers with SMI were able to quit smoking with medication treatment; none of the medication treatments resulted in more side effects than placebo; and varenicline plus behavioral counseling was associated with the highest quit rates for all three groups:

- People with mood disorders (30% quit)

- People with *psychotic disorders* (23% quit)

- People without psychiatric illness (38% quit)

The EAGLES trial demonstrated that smoking-cessation medications combined with behavioral counseling are effective, safe, and well-tolerated by smokers with and without psychiatric illness.

> ### ❧ Key Point
>
> Smokers with and without a SMI have greater success with quitting when they receive smoking-cessation counseling with an effective smoking-cessation medication, such as varenicline (Chantix®), nicotine replacement therapy (typically patch plus lozenge), or bupropion (Wellbutrin®/Zyban®). All smokers have the best chance of quitting when they are given a smoking-cessation medication.

Getting help for smoking might start with talking to your psychiatric care team or your *primary care physician* (PCP) about which smoking-cessation medication your PCP would recommend for you and how you can get counseling support for smoking cessation. A common misconception is that a person must be completely ready to stop smoking before taking a smoking-cessation medication (Prochaska, 2011). In actuality, some medications reduce *cravings* and other *withdrawal* symptoms, which helps a person cut down on how much he or she smokes, and it builds the smoker's confidence that he or she will be able to make a quit attempt over several weeks.

> ### ❧ Key Point
>
> You do not have to be 100% ready to quit to start a smoking-cessation treatment. Sometimes, starting treatment helps people decrease cravings and build confidence.

Several free telephone and online resources are available to help smokers stop smoking. Check out https://everytrycounts.betobaccofree.hhs.gov/ for information and text messaging support designed to help smokers who are ready to take a small step toward quitting smoking (such as planning not to smoke for two hours). You can also find helpful information if you are ready to make a quit attempt. Another resource is your state's quit line, staffed by counselors specifically trained to help smokers quit; call 800-QUIT-NOW (800-784-8669). Perhaps the most important thing is to remind yourself that with the right treatment, you can quit smoking.

What Can I Do to Try to Eat Healthier?

Although many people with and without SMI say that their most important health goal is to lose weight, losing weight is the result of behavior change, so a more precise behavioral goal is to eat in such a way as to reduce calorie intake (and increase activity levels). The best way to do this is to decrease the intake of unhealthy foods (foods that are high in fat and sugar) and increase the intake of healthy foods that are high in nutrients and fiber (such as vegetables and whole fruits). Investigators at Johns Hopkins conducted a landmark study showing that overweight people with SMI could lose weight by their increasing activity levels and receiving support to follow a few simple dietary guidelines: 1) reduce caloric intake by avoiding sugar drinks and "junk food"; 2) eat five fruits and vegetables a day; and 3) choose smart portions and snacks (Daumit et al, 2013). One of the highest-yield strategies for weight loss is to cut out or dramatically reduce sugar-sweetened beverages. Many people do not realize that there is the equivalent of approximately 15 teaspoons of sugar in one 16-ounce bottle of soda or juice. (That's almost 1 teaspoon per ounce!) If you have one large soda every day and then switch to flavored seltzer water or water without making any other changes, you could lose about three pounds a month. Some people with SMI live in *residential programs* or eat in *clubhouses* or rehabilitation settings. In these cases, it is important that people advocate for themselves for changes in the food environment that will help them lose weight, such as increasing the availability of whole fruits, vegetables, and non-sugar containing beverages.

> ### ⅍ Key Point
>
> A high-yield strategy for weight loss is to eliminate sugar-containing drinks (sodas, juices, sweet tea, sweetened coffee drinks). A person who drinks two sodas a day and makes this single change could lose approximately three pounds per month without doing anything else.

Changing the habit of eating fast food can be challenging because fast food is easy to obtain, inexpensive, and tastes good. Learning how to read nutrition information or to search online for information about the healthiest options at your favorite food restaurant can help you select healthier choices.

Portion sizes that are too large is another bad habit. New guidelines suggest that people should fill half of their plates with fruits and vegetables, and one quarter plate each should be devoted to protein and grains. (See www.choosemyplate.gov for current USDA recommendations, including personalized resources for your age, gender, weight, and height.)

Type II diabetes (non-insulin dependent diabetes) can be reversed by making long-term changes in your diet and activity level; these changes result in weight loss. Many people with SMI who have type II diabetes are not aware that they can take steps (beyond medication) to manage and potentially eliminate their diabetes. Moreover, they are often unaware of the risks of chronic, poorly controlled type II diabetes, such as high blood pressure, heart disease, stroke, vision problems, foot ulcers, kidney damage, and nerve damage. Also, many people are not aware of the risk of progressing to need insulin for type II diabetes.

What Can I Do to Be More Active?

Many people associate being more active with going to the gym, running, or engaging in other vigorous exercise. Because many people cannot picture themselves doing these things, they wind up not being active at all. However, any decrease in sedentary behavior effectively increases activity levels. For example, you are reducing your sedentary behavior and increasing your activity level if you spend more time walking around your apartment and spend less time in bed or spend more time standing than sitting. Some data suggests that people who experience the most benefit from being less sedentary are those who go from being almost completely inactive to doing a little bit of activity. One effective way of helping people become more active is to teach them how to quantify their steps each day using a *pedometer* or their smartphones, which can record the number of steps per day over several weeks or more. It is helpful to get in the habit of carrying your pedometer without trying to change activity levels and then compare the average number of steps per day as a baseline from which to increase it by some agreed upon increment. Using this method and some encouragement, even people who are relatively inactive often increase their step counts by 2,000 steps per day over a period of several months, which translates into more calories burned and improved cardiovascular fitness.

❈ Key Point

Do not be paralyzed by the magnitude of the challenge if you are currently inactive. Start with small steps and then build on them. Be realistic about what you can do and start slowly (one day a week); doing more than you can sustain will lead you to abandon the effort quickly. Recall if you had been more active. Can you imagine becoming like that again?

How Can I Improve My Sleep?

Sleep problems are extremely common in people with SMI (Subramaniam et al, 2018), and they have been associated with more severe psychiatric symptoms, including thoughts of suicide (Miller et al, 2019). Sleep problems are often an early warning sign of *relapse*. Because sleep is important for both physical and mental wellbeing, information on what sleep problems can signify, and suggestions for how to address them, should be provided. Sleep problems take a variety of forms, such as difficulty falling asleep, difficulty staying asleep, sleeping too much, feeling tired despite sleeping, and having a decreased need for sleep. Sleep issues could be related to what you do (or don't do during the day). Sleep issues can be related to symptoms, such as depression or anxiety, be related to medication side effects, or be related to a lack of healthy sleep behaviors, also known as "*sleep hygiene.*"

Improving sleep hygiene is often a good place to start if you are thinking about taking steps to improve the quality of your sleep. This includes a range of behaviors, such as waking up at the same time every morning, engaging in some exercise during the day, refraining from napping, starting a relaxing bedtime routine that does not involve looking at computer screens or accessing upsetting information, and limiting your caffeine intake during the afternoons (see Table 11-2 for a list of ways to improve sleep behaviors). Sometimes, people notice that they only have difficulty sleeping in their own beds; when they go to a hotel or stay at a family member's house, they sleep well and feel rested. If this is the case, you might consider whether you have developed "*psychophysiological insomnia*" (learning to associate your own bed with difficulty sleeping). To break this cycle, you should practice good sleep hygiene and also get out of bed if you find yourself lying awake and tossing and turning for more than 30 minutes. Getting out of bed and doing something relaxing in another room and returning to bed when you feel sleepy is a key strategy for reconditioning the association between your bed and sleep.

Table 11-2: Dos and Don'ts of Sleep Behaviors (Sleep Hygiene)

Dos
• Go to bed and get up at the same time every day, regardless of how much sleep you got the night before.
• Exercise during the day so that you will feel tired at night.
• Choose something relaxing to do at least 30 minutes before bed (such as reading a book, taking a bath or warm shower, or listening to music).
• Take medications as prescribed.
• Talk with your doctor about sleep problems.

Don'ts
• Nap during the day, even if you didn't sleep well the previous night.
• Spend more than 30 minutes at a time lying in bed trying to get to sleep; instead, get up and go into another room and do something relaxing.
• Drink anything with caffeine after 3 p.m.
• Smoke right before going to bed.
• Watch anything on TV that might be exciting or upsetting before going to bed.
• Talk about upsetting topics with other people before going to bed.

Other resources:
Sleep Medicine Center at Stanford University (https://stanfordhealthcare.org/medical-conditions/sleep/insomnia/treatments.html).
Linde S, Hauri P: *No More Sleepless Nights*. United Kingdom: Wiley; 1996.

Sleep problems are often a sign that sleep behaviors could use some fine-turning, and they are a sign of depression, anxiety, or mania. For example, early morning awakening (when you consistently wake up earlier than you would like to) is a characteristic of depression. This is in contrast to having a decreased need for sleep, a symptom of mania, in which you might feel rested after only 4–5 hours of sleep. Difficulty staying asleep (*middle insomnia*), getting to sleep (initial insomnia), or excessive daytime sleepiness may also be signs of depression or anxiety (see Chapter 10 for suggested strategies for managing these symptoms). A *sleep disorder*, such as *sleep apnea*, or *narcolepsy* can be another possible contributor to excessive daytime fatigue. Another contributor to excessive daytime fatigue is being overly sedated by a medication or using prescribed (such as benzodiazepines) or illicit drugs that interfere with the quality of your sleep.

Another type of sleep problem is sleeping mostly the day and being awake at night, *delayed sleep phase syndrome*, which can result in difficulties waking up in time to meet responsibilities, attend appointments, and interact with others. This type of sleep pattern can develop in response to other symptoms, such as paranoia or *negative symptoms*, and can be a strategy used to "shut out the world" and reduce stimulation. Thus, this pattern can be more upsetting to family members than to you. Family members might miss interacting with you and be concerned about the adverse effect of this sleep pattern on your social and role functioning. To address this issue, you might need more treatment for these underlying symptoms, and you might need to develop personally relevant goals that give you a reason to get up in the morning.

> ### ⅔ Key Point
>
> If you sleep too much because there is nothing to get up for, focusing on "insomnia" at night is not going to be helpful. If you are simply not tired when you are trying to fall asleep, your routines might need to change, and you might need to establish a reason to get up in the morning. Families can help change sleeping habits by scheduling shared activities with you at a reasonable time (not at 7:30 in the morning).

Ground-breaking research suggests that when offered treatment for a range of co-occurring issues, many people with SMI choose to work on their sleep (Freeman et al, 2019). Also, insomnia interventions might decrease both insomnia and *psychotic* symptoms (*hallucinations* and *delusions*), which suggests sleep difficulties should be a specific focus of both medication and psychosocial treatments for people with SMI (Blanchard et al, 2020a, 2020b).

Which Preventative Health Appointments Should I Keep Up with?

Given the higher rates of *co-morbid* medical conditions, such as diabetes, high *cholesterol*, and diabetes among people with SMI, it is perhaps even more important that people with SMI access routine and specialty medical care. However, people with SMI are less likely to receive recommended cancer screenings (such as *mammograms*, *prostate exams*, or *cervical cancer screening*), which might be in some cases a function of their not seeing their PCPs as frequently as people without a SMI (Hwong et al, 2019; Tuesley et al, 2019).

They are also much less likely to attend dental appointments, even when they have insurance that covers dental cleanings (Hall et al, 2018). In terms of dental care, the use of medications (such as *anticholinergic drugs*, *antihistamines*, *antidepressants*, *antipsychotics*, *antihypertensives*, *diuretics*, and *antiparkinsonian drugs*) that induce dry mouth *(xerogenic medications)*, increase the risk of dental problems in this population and place an even higher importance on preventative dental care. Additionally, poor attention to good *oral hygiene* contributes to the elevated rates of dental problems (including cavities and the increased risk of losing all one's teeth) in those with SMI (Kieley et al, 2015). Barriers include low perceived importance, transportation issues, and fears of visiting the dentist. Eye care also suffers from similar neglect because eye exams are often somewhat separate from routine medical care.

Because people with SMI receiving treatment are likely to see their psychiatric care teams much more often than their primary care teams, models of care that integrate primary care and psychiatric care hold promise for this group. Some of these models co-locate psychiatric and primary care services, while others set up designated primary care services in psychiatric clinics, which facilitates communication among health care providers. Still others use *reverse integrated care* models, in which the psychiatric team increasingly assumes responsibility for monitoring of common medical conditions.

✺ Key Point

Your psychiatrist might be in a good position to help you with some aspects of your medical care, including doing some tests in the psychiatric clinic. For example, if you take antipsychotics, the psychiatric clinic should be organized in a way to help you keep track of medical monitoring for diabetes.

How Can My Primary Care Doctor or Psychiatrist Help Me?

PCPs and *psychiatrists* can provide information and guidance regarding which health problems are important to address and whether the problems should be addressed with medications and/or behavioral changes. Physicians and their staff can help you overcome barriers to medical care when you share information about what is getting in the way of obtaining the medical care you deserve. Doctors' offices can arrange for free transportation for you and set up appointment reminders. (You can choose to have these directed to a family member who can help you remember.) Doctor's offices also help you overcome some of your fears about upcoming medical procedures by talking about them with you, providing additional staff to support you through appointments, and/or prescribing short-term medications to alleviate anxiety.

Your doctors can help you identify other resources and supports for your health goals. They can provide referrals to a variety of services, including a *nutritionist*, a diabetes education and self-management group, weight loss groups, and *physical therapy* (PT). If your doctor thinks your sleep difficulties are suggestive of a sleep disorder, he or she can refer you for an *overnight sleep study* so that this issue can be diagnosed and treated effectively.

Open communication with your doctors about your experience with medication side effects is a part of a collaborative care model. Your doctor can offer suggestions about what can be done to alter the medication regimen to decrease side effects. This might mean a switch to another medication, the addition of a medication, or a dose reduction. Also, there are likely behavioral changes that you can make to address these side effects. You can take an active stance in managing or preventing these health problems, even when the medication is contributing to them.

What Is a Health Care Proxy and How Do I Put This in Place?

A *health care proxy* is a legal document in which you name someone you trust to make medical decisions for you if you become unable to communicate your wishes (such as if you were unconscious or in a coma). You must be a competent adult to complete this form, and you must designate a *health care agent*. In most cases, a family member will be this agent. The health care agent should be fully informed about your wishes, so before completing the form, you should meet with a health care provider, advocate, or lawyer to guide this discussion. Your health care agent cannot act on your behalf until your doctor documents that you are unable to speak for yourself. Your health care agent can access your medical information and will be given information about the risks and benefits of treatment; also, your health care agent will be given the power to discontinue any treatment by your doctor. If you give your health care agent full authority to act for you, he or she can consent to refuse medical treatment, including treatment that would keep you alive. These documents are available online and vary from state to state. The document must be signed by you and must either be notarized or signed by a witness, or witnesses, who are not your health care agent. Once you have completed the requirements of this form, you should submit it to your doctor or the medical records office of the hospital where you receive treatment. You can revoke a health care proxy at any time if you are judged to be competent to do so at the time.

⚘ Key Point

Make sure you understand the laws and requirements in your state regarding the appointment of a health care proxy. Having a health care proxy is important and should not be delayed. You never know when you are going to be incapacitated. It helps everybody if it is in place—including you so that your wishes be implemented. Otherwise, people may have to make decisions that you would never have wanted.

Many people are unaware that there is a psychiatric arm of the health care proxy that functions in the same way and pertains specifically to mental health treatment. In this case, you can designate someone to make decisions about the treatment you would want to receive/not receive in the event of mental health symptoms that make you unable to make decisions for yourself. Unlike health care proxies, which are supported by all states, only a limited number of states recognize psychiatric *advance directives*.

How Can My Family or Others Close to Me Help?

Family members can help by making themselves open and available to the role of "buddy"/ supporter to help you make progress on your identified health goals. For example, if you want to become more active, you and a family member could start the routine of an after-dinner walk around the neighborhood together and even, perhaps, start recording your steps per day on a calendar together and celebrate milestones. Family members can serve as good food shopping or cooking companions, so if your goal is to buy healthier food or to learn to make healthier meals, these could be activities in which you enlist the help of a supportive other. It is important that you have agreed to accept this help and that it maps onto your goals. It's is easy to imagine how pressure from family members about these issues could produce negative results, including criticism, as opposed to support. At times, however, there are ways in which family members are unhelpful or enable negative health behaviors, such as by purchasing cigarettes, alcohol, or fast food for you when doing so is not in your best health interest or by providing you with money that you use for these purposes. In this case, the family might want to work with a family therapist to modify these patterns so that they are not contributing to health problems and a lower quality of life for you. Also, there might be some situations in which you are not attending to a health condition due to an inability to care for yourself or a lack of *competence* to make medical decisions that is related to your psychiatric condition. In these cases, a psychiatric hospitalization might be necessary to stabilize the psychiatric condition, and legal *guardianship* might be considered.

In general, family members need to strike the right balance between offering support for health goals and supporting your autonomy. However, family members should not assume that you do not want help, just because you have not asked. For example, offering help with things like transportation to a medical appointment, using an app to track sleep or food or activity, or with figuring out a daily schedule to create a better sense of meaning or purpose is often welcomed, as long as it is offered in a kind, supportive, and non-judgmental way.

CAN I BE HOPEFUL ABOUT RECOVERY?

Oliver Freudenreich, MD; Corinne Cather, PhD; and
Theodore A. Stern, MD

In This Chapter

What Is My Prognosis?

Among the most important questions that anyone with a *serious mental illness* (SMI), like *schizophrenia* or *bipolar disorder*, will have is, "What should I expect?" In medicine, the term *prognosis* is used to predict the probable course of a disease and its outcome, including the chance for a full *recovery*. Prognosis is closely tied to treatment: Prognosis differs depending on the type and quality of treatment provided.

Key questions with regard to prognosis include: "Prognosis with regards to what outcome?" and, "What difference will treatment make compared to doing nothing?" The outcome that interests most patients depends on the disease. For many diseases, people simply want to have their *symptoms* disappear *(symptomatic remission)* and return to their pre-illness life *(functional remission)*. For other diseases, the stakes regarding outcome are higher. Patients with cancer often ask: "What are my chances for survival–with and without treatment?" People with more chronic conditions like orthopedic problems might ask: "What are the chances that I will play sports again, with or without treatment (such as orthopedic surgery) and if different treatments can be considered (such as surgery versus physical therapy)?" For chronic illnesses (such as *multiple sclerosis* [MS]), it is also important to ask about short-term outcomes as compared to long-term outcomes. Sometimes, the cure (such as the use of high-dose *steroids*) is worse than the disease: Treatment may not offer much more of a benefit over doing nothing, but it adds to the side-effect burden of treatment. Watchful waiting can then be a reasonable strategy. People with a SMI often wonder if they can return to college or work, live independently, and get married. Although patients and families often do not think about asking about the prognosis *quo ad vitam* (with regard to life), this is also important when facing psychological and psychiatric disorders. Death from suicide or from accidental death while *psychotic*, for example, is an outcome that may be averted with treatment.

Unfortunately, the adage, often (mis)attributed to Yogi Berra, "It's tough to make predictions, particularly about the future," applies to prognosis in medicine: Individual outcomes for those with a SMI can be quite varied, and making predictions about the prognosis is fraught with difficulties. That said, if a psychiatric disorder is severe, treatment is likely to make a substantial difference. In large groups of people with schizophrenia, people who receive no treatment are often those with the worst outcomes, including premature death. For people who seek treatment, symptomatic remission—or at least a substantial improvement in symptoms—is a realistic goal, while functional remission remains more elusive.

What Is the Natural Course of Serious Mental Illness?

The so-called *natural course of disease* is an ideal: "What does a disease look like if we just observe it and do nothing?" However, such a situation is highly abstract because all diseases occur in the context of time and place. Cultural practices, for example, can significantly affect outcome (Hopper and Wanderling, 2000). Nevertheless, it is useful to look at possible outcomes for groups of people.

If we use schizophrenia as an example, a certain percentage of patients—perhaps as many as 20%—will do rather well after receiving treatment for a first-episode of psychosis. These people return to their baseline with treatment; even after treatment has been discontinued, they continue to do well and do not require ongoing care (Volavka and Vevera, 2018). One study that followed a group of patients with schizophrenia who were discharged from a Vermont state hospital during the era of *deinstitutionalization* found that most made significant improvements in their lives and function since their discharge decades earlier (Harding et al, 1987). This historic study was important because it questioned the pessimistic view of SMI as a fixed entity, with no chance of improvement.

Using schizophrenia as an example again, a more fine-grained view of prognosis can be viewed graphically by using four quadrants. Those in a "good-prognosis" quadrant have one to three psychotic episodes from which they completely recover, with little need for care when not having an episode(s). Those in the "poor-prognosis" quadrant experience serious and ongoing symptoms that might not respond to treatment; they might need to be hospitalized chronically in some form of institutional setting. The other two quadrants are comprised by people with some symptoms and functional difficulties. Depending on the severity of their symptoms and disability, one group will live independently while the other group will need more help from their families or from state agencies. Unfortunately, it is difficult to know from the beginning of a SMI what an individual's course will look like. The outcome is neither as fixed nor, as pre-determined as the term, "natural course," implies, as biological, and other factors, such as adherence to treatment and substance use, determine the extent of recovery.

 Key Point

In psychiatry, long-term follow-up is needed to understand the outcome of a disorder like schizophrenia.

Is Schizophrenia a Progressive Brain Disease?

Schizophrenia is not a progressive brain disease (in the sense that the term is used in *neurology*) (Zipursky et al, 2013) like *Alzheimer's disease*. It does not have increasing *cognitive deficits* and a complete need for care after a decade of the illness. In fact, *cognitive difficulties* that are characteristic of schizophrenia are largely present during the first episode of psychosis and remain stable until an advanced age when the disease takes its toll (Sheffield et al, 2018). Figure 12-1 depicts a series of psychotic episodes with a plateau of function. The figure also portrays graphically that each relapse makes it harder to achieve the prior level of function. Reducing the number of episodes with treatment during a critical phase (for example, where interventions might change the trajectory toward better long-term outcomes) allows for the best possible recovery.

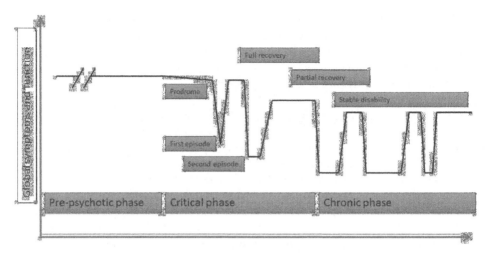

Figure 12-1: Highly schematic outcome of schizophrenia.

Can I Be Cured?

By definition, SMI persists and is unlikely to "go away" on its own. However, treatment does not cure SMI. While many treatments in medicine are curative, treatments for psychiatric conditions typically target symptoms or aim to prevent future episodes of illness. Treatments for SMI, like schizophrenia or bipolar disorder, are usually not *disease-modifying*. That is, they do not alter the biology of the illness. This should not be too surprising given that SMI is rooted in brain development. Curing such disorders will require, at least in part, a partial reversal of the *neurodevelopment* that went awry; unfortunately, this is not currently possible. However, early intervention and *prevention* offer some promise for changing the natural history of neurodevelopmental disorders like schizophrenia—but this will need to be initiated **before** the disorders become clinically apparent.

> **⁑ Key Point**
>
> While a cure is not possible for most people diagnosed with SMI, these disorders can be managed. Good management improves prognosis.

What Factors Influence My Prognosis?

Prognosis is influenced by both *biological* and *non-biological factors*. Table 12-1 depicts an important message: While biology is important, many factors are under a person's or society's control and can influence outcome.

Table 12-1: Contributors to "Poor Outcomes"

Non-Modifiable	Modifiable
Unresponsive biology	• *Non-adherence* to medications
	• Substance use
	• Delayed care
	• Time spent in hospitals due to lack of treatment
	• Time spending idle at home
	• Poor engagement in psychiatric care
	• Poor physical health
	• Smoking
	• Poor access to care
	• Substandard psychiatric care
	• Social determinants of health

Substance use and non-adherence with treatment are probably the most important reasons to explain a less-than-optimal outcome. Those are potentially modifiable factors that should to be addressed, regardless of one's biology. Persistent substance use undermines medication efficacy and even the most biologically-responsive form of schizophrenia will have a poor outcome if treatment is simply not used (for example, because of medication non-adherence). Other factors also interfere with recovery and are related to treatment resources offered by our society. Unfortunately, geographical differences abound with regard to access to resources that can help people with SMI and their families manage SMI. Remember to use the right treatment, at the right time, at the right intensity, and at the right place. One size does not fit all. For example, a young person who dropped out of college because of a psychotic episode needs different treatment and support than does a mid-career professional who struggles at work because of chronic depression.

> **⚘ Key Point**
>
> Outcomes for people with SMI are dependent upon a complex mixture of biology, substance use, medical co-morbidities, medication adherence, and access to high-quality treatment and rehabilitation services.

What Can I Do to Live Well with a Serious Mental Illness?

Just because a cure might not be in the cards, you should recognize that you are not helpless. Seeking and accepting treatment for SMI are first steps that might not come easily. However, they are a necessary starting point. Once engaged in treatment, there are a variety of things that you can do to have your best possible life, and there are many things that you can do that will hinder your recovery. For example, modifying your self-defeating beliefs and stopping counterproductive behaviors can make a huge difference. Concrete examples of these strategies are summarized in Table 12-2.

Table 12-2: Living with a SMI

Accepting psychiatric help
• Accept the need for treatment and seek the right treatment*
• Assemble a treatment team
• Build routines regarding taking medications
Educating yourself
• *Psychoeducation*
Building new skills
• Build coping skills, like stress management
• Build new psychological skills and *resilience*
• Consider a career change
Living healthy
• Stay physically healthy
• Build routines that include good sleep habits
• Do not use drugs
• Use alcohol in moderation only
Building a support network
• Accept help from family members (and negotiate what kind of help)
• Ask family members for help (including for example sibling, not just parents)
• Use a peer network
Planning for the future
• Develop a plan about school or work
• Have an emergency plan
• Develop a plan about where to live

*Phase-specific: the right treatment, at the right time, of the right intensity, in the right setting.

Will I Always Have to Take Medications?

SMI requires management for years, if not decades. While some people do well with intermittent treatment, most people require *maintenance treatment* to prevent symptom *relapse* (of psychosis, mania, or depression). The types of medications used to prevent relapse depend on the condition you have. For bipolar disorder, *lithium* and other *mood stabilizers* are used; for schizophrenia, *antipsychotics* are prescribed; and for severe depression, *anti-depressants* are employed. Once you have had more than one episode of illness, your risk of having a relapse is high. Although it is counterintuitive, having done well for years with maintenance treatment for schizophrenia does not mean that you do no longer need medication (Leucht et al, 2012). Because the biology of the disorder has not changed with treatment (meaning the treatment is not disease-modifying), your risk of relapse remains.

The decision to continue taking medications becomes clearer once you have had several episodes of illness because there is a high risk of relapse after medications have been stopped. One of the most difficult decisions for you and your treaters to make is deciding what to do after a first-episode of illness. At that point, it is unclear if the illness is one with a high relapse risk. Some people (roughly 20%) with an episode of psychosis will not have a second episode. Unfortunately, the characteristics of those in this group are unknown.

After having had more experience with an illness, many people realize that whether to take medications (or not) is not the most important question. Instead, the key question is, "How can I have the best life possible despite my illness." Medications are tools that should be used optimally.

Why Is My Attitude Towards My Illness Important?

When bad things happen to us—like developing SMI—we can develop a variety of reactions, such as, we can be angry at our fate, decry the unfairness of it, or blame others. While understandable (and normal), these views make you the victim of circumstances and attempt to take away the control you have over your life. Unfortunately, bitterness and anger are paralyzing and are unlikely to make you feel good about your situation. At some point, a different world view that puts you in charge of your life and your destiny is desirable to help you come to terms with the reality that you have a SMI and that you should face it constructively. Such a mindset does not just happen. Time and therapy can help you accept your illness. It will also set the stage for using the tools of treatment (such as medications) as you start to see the "big picture."

Victor Frankl, a Viennese psychiatrist who survived life in a concentration camp, recognized that one can be deprived of almost anything by other human beings except for the attitude one has toward a situation (Frankl, 1959). This psychological power allows people to find reasons to live despite dire circumstances and to face a psychiatric illness with a positive attitude. While this may sound banal, many people discover that changing their attitude toward their illness is among the most important interventions.

✴ Key Point

You can choose to have a positive attitude toward your illness. You can choose to be embittered and angry about your fate, or you can choose to accept the realities of having a psychiatric illness that you did not seek or deserve—and make the best of your situation.

What Is Recovery?

The term "recovery" means different things to different people. Recovery is a term embraced by professional and non-professional organization alike, which subscribe to a "recovery-oriented philosophy." In the extreme, recovery is used to mean "cure." However, it might be more realistic and helpful to view recovery as a journey, rather than a destination (Deegan, 1997). During this journey, you can learn how to live with an illness and how to overcome *stigma* (including *self-stigma*).

One definition of recovery is pragmatic and acknowledges the reality of SMI as a group of chronic and partially-biological conditions for which we have no cure—but that also maintains the hope that a better life is possible. Recovery can be viewed as a mindset and psychological process that allows people to recover a sense of personhood that is not merely defined by having a SMI. People with SMI are friends, neighbors, co-workers, and citizens. Importantly, having recovered does not mean that you are cured and it does not mean that no additional help (including medications that are tools for the pursuit of life goals) is needed (Deegan et al, 2017).

> ### ⚘ Key Point
>
> At its core, recovery is a deeply personal experience; recovery goals are defined by you—not by society or by your family.

What Does Successful Recovery Look Like?

It is helpful to ask yourself: "What is a good outcome for a SMI that might not go away?" If a *restitutio ad integrum* is not possible because of the *neurobiology* of the illness, what outcomes are possible that might be "good enough" for a good life? This question enables discussions about a realistic assessment about the length and commitment needed and the type of goals you can pursue when a cure is not possible.

> ### ⚘ Key Point
>
> You should discuss your vision of recovery with your treatment team and agree on treatment goals. Is recovery an all-or-nothing outcome, or is it something in-between? Is it a process? If it is, how long will it take? What matters most to you in your vision of recovery?

What Can My Family Do to Help Me with My Recovery?

Some families are "naturals" in helping their loved one regain a sense of purpose after being diagnosed with a SMI. Other families struggle to adjust the expectations they had for their loved one, often putting pressure on them to succeed in unrealistic and counterproductive ways. Many families, with some help and education, learn to help each other. Encouraging your family to learn about your condition is a good place to start. Some discussion and negotiation about what kind of help you would like your family to provide can guide your parents or siblings about how to be helpful (and when to leave you alone). Most families remain connected despite the ups-and-downs of SMI. Remaining in touch and not "burning bridges" goes a long way toward mending family discord when it occurs. There is no substitute for a supportive family network. You should encourage your family to seek help and to avoid burnout.

Why Should I Be Hopeful About My Life?

Hope is a crucial ingredient in difficult circumstances—like having a SMI. Hopefulness and optimism will help you to tolerate the course corrections that are needed and to have the energy for the long and difficult road that lies ahead.

Many people and their families have carved out good lives for themselves—despite everything. While adjustments might be needed, new goals can bring happiness. Moreover, medicines now available are better tolerated than were medicines used decades ago. Research has identified psychological treatments that can help you recover more completely. Society, while imperfect, has made progress by including people with a SMI in community life in ways that were unthinkable just a few decades ago. The peer movement and the many books in which people have shared their stories of recovery give us hope that we will continue to destigmatize SMI and that those with SMI can live fulfilling lives. Every clinician can see human resilience and the human spirit in their interactions with their patients—if he or she pays attention.

❄ Key Point

Per aspera ad astra (Latin for, 'through hardship to the stars") captures the reality of the stony road to recovery for many people with SMI. It will not be easy, but life does not have to come to an end: It might merely be different than planned and have new possibilities and experiences. Small victories happen all the time and should be celebrated.

GLOSSARY

Abnormal Involuntary Movement Scale (AIMS): The standard rating scale to screen for and track the course of tardive dyskinesia (TD).

Academic center: An organization that is affiliated with an academic institution that provides rehabilitation services and often also conducts research on these services.

Acceptance and commitment therapy (ACT): A treatment that encourages people to embrace their thoughts and feelings, rather than fighting or feeling guilty about them.

Accountable care organizations (ACOs): ACOs are groups of doctors, hospitals, and other health care providers who come together voluntarily to provide coordinated care to Medicare patients.

Acute: A condition that is severe or sudden in onset.

Acute psychosis: A mental state with new-onset delusions or hallucinations.

Acute dystonic reaction: A side effect of antipsychotics involving sudden and sustained muscle contractions, particularly of the neck (torticollis), and other body parts, such as the eyes (oculogyric crisis), which occurs shortly after beginning an antipsychotic agent; it is rare with the newer antipsychotics.

Addiction: A chronic and severe form of a substance use disorder in which a person has lost control over his or her use of a substance, resulting in the compulsive use despite adverse consequences. Behavioral addictions apply the addiction concept to behaviors (such as gambling).

Adherence: Following treatment recommendations; it usually refers to taking medications as prescribed by a doctor.

Advance directive: A written statement of a person's wishes regarding medical treatment that often includes a living will that is made to ensure that those wishes are carried out should the person be unable to communicate them to a doctor.

Affective symptoms: Mood symptoms, such as symptoms of depression or mania.

Affective illness: Mental health disorders, such as major depression or bipolar disorder, which are characterized by disturbances in mood, thoughts, and feelings.

Affirmative businesses (social firms): Businesses created with the specific mission of employing people with disabilities to provide a needed product or service.

Agoraphobia: A disorder characterized by abnormal fear of being helpless in a situation from which escape can be difficult or embarrassing and resulting in the avoidance of public situations from which escape can be difficult, such as standing in line or being in a crowd.

Agranulocytosis: Also known as severe neutropenia. It denotes a severe reduction in a type of white blood cell (particularly neutrophils) that are necessary to fight infections. It is a dangerous medication side effect, particularly of the antipsychotic clozapine.

Akathisia: An unpleasant medication side effect with anxiety and restlessness that compels a person to move about and pace; it literally means "the inability to sit still."

Alcoholics anonymous (AA): A worldwide, voluntary organization of men and women who, through a 12-step program, seek to help each other stay sober and learn to live healthy, fulfilling lives. Founded in the United States in 1935, AA is the oldest, largest, and best-known self-help organization.

Algorithm: In medicine, a set of rules (such as a decision tree) to facilitate diagnosis or treatment of a condition.

Allergic reaction: A side effect (often with itching, hives, or difficulty breathing) in which the immune system has mistakenly reacted to a medication, recognizing it as something "foreign."

Altman Self-Rating Mania Scale: A five-item self-rating mania scale that is designed to assess the presence and/or severity of manic symptoms.

Alzheimer's disease: The most common form of progressive dementia.

American Psychiatric Association (APA): The main professional organization of psychiatrists and psychiatric trainees in the United States.

Americans with Disabilities Act (ADA): A civil rights law enacted in 1990 that prohibits discrimination based on a disability.

Amotivation: The state of lacking motivation to engage in activity.

Angiotensin-converting enzyme (ACE) inhibitor: A class of medications used to treat hypertension and heart failure.

Anomie: A term used to indicate social instability, where a society breaks down because of the lack of social standards or shared ideals.

Anosognosia: A deficit of self-awareness.

Anticholinergic drugs: A class of medications sometimes used when starting high-potency, first-generation antipsychotic medications to reduce the incidence of Parkinsonism or dystonic reactions (extrapyramidal symptoms [EPS]) or to manage Parkinsonism as part of ongoing treatment. Anticholinergic medications can cause substantial side-effects themselves, such as urinary retention, constipation, blurred vision, and cognitive impairment.

Antidepressants: A class of psychiatric medications used to treat depression, pain, insomnia, and anxiety.

Antiepileptic drugs (AEDs): A class of medication used to treat seizures, epilepsy, certain types of pain, and mood disorders. Many, but not all, AEDs are also effective as mood-stabilizers.

Antihistamines: Any drugs or agents that inhibit the effects of histamine at central or peripheral histamine receptors, especially H1 receptors. Drugs in this class might have sedative effects and are often a common component of over-the-counter sleeping aids. Some of the drugs in this class are used in the treatment of allergic reactions.

Antihypertensive drugs: A class of medications used to treat high blood pressure (hypertension); some drugs in this class, such as beta-blockers, are sometimes used to treat social phobias (such as stage fright) or akathisia.

Anti-inflammatory: A medication or application (such as ice) used to reduce inflammation.

Antiparkinsonian drugs: Medications used in the treatment of Parkinson's disease, a progressive disease of the nervous system marked by tremor, muscular rigidity, and slow, imprecise movements that is caused by degeneration of the basal ganglia in the brain and a deficiency of the neurotransmitter dopamine. These drugs can also be used to treat motor abnormalities caused by side effects of antipsychotic medications, which block dopamine.

Antipsychotic treatment: Medications and other somatic treatments, such as electroconvulsive therapy, that reduce manifestations of psychosis.

Antipsychotics: A group of psychiatric medications that treat psychosis, as well as nausea and vomiting. All currently available antipsychotics are anti-dopaminergic agents (for example, they block dopamine-2 receptors in the brain).

Anxiety disorder: Any of several psychological disorders (such as panic disorder, phobias, or generalized anxiety disorder) in which anxiety and avoidance are predominant features.

Anxiety: A non-specific state characterized by worry, apprehension, and unease. It can be a normal reaction to stress or indicate a psychiatric problem.

Anxiety sensitivity: The fear of behaviors or sensations associated with the experience of anxiety, and a misinterpretation of such sensations as dangerous.

Anxiolytic: A class of medications used to alleviate anxiety and insomnia.

Aptitude tests: Tests that assess a person's capacity to learn new material, succeed in school, or acquire specific skills for their job. Aptitude tests differ from achievement tests (that measure what someone has already learned).

Aripiprazole (Abilify®): A widely used antipsychotic and mood stabilizer.

Assertive Community Treatment (ACT): An evidence-based practice that offers treatment, rehabilitation, and support services using a person-centered, recovery-based approach, to people who have been diagnosed with serious mental illness (SMI). Services are often delivered in the individual's home or community (see also PACT).

Assertiveness training: A skills training approach that teaches the respectful expression of thoughts, feelings, and needs.

Attention deficit disorder (ADD): A disorder that arises in childhood with prominent difficulties with attention. Many people with this disorder are hyperactive and impulsive, accounting for the condition's official name, attention-deficit/hyperactivity disorder (ADHD).

Attention deficit hyperactivity disorder (ADHD): A condition characterized by difficulty in attention/concentration, impulsivity, and hyperactivity.

Attention re-training: The re-training of automatic attentional processes by focusing on alternative stimuli.

Auditory hallucinations: Hearing voices or sounds without an external stimulus; one of the major symptoms of psychosis.

Autism spectrum disorder (ASD): An umbrella term for disorders (of which the prototype is autism) of social interaction and communication. The severity spectrum spans high-functioning autism (also called Asperger syndrome) and children with severe disabilities.

Automatic thoughts: Instantaneous, habitual, and non-conscious thoughts that affect a person's mood and actions.

Avatar therapy: A therapy approach (invented by Julian Leff in 2008) in which people who hear voices have a dialogue with a digital representation (avatar) of their presumed persecutor, voiced by the therapist so that the avatar responds by becoming less hostile and concedes power over the course of therapy.

Avoidance: The act or practice of keeping away from or withdrawing from something undesirable.

Avolition: A lack of interest or engagement in goal-directed behavior.

Basal ganglia: A group of brain structures deep inside the brain that regulate movements. A variety of neurological disorders, like Huntington's disease and Parkinson's disease, which involve the basal ganglia. Movement disorders associated with use of antipsychotic drugs act on the basal ganglia.

Baseline labs: Laboratory tests (often blood tests) that are obtained prior to beginning treatment or starting a medication.

Behavioral activation: A therapeutic intervention that is often used to treat depression. Behavioral activation aims to increase engagement in adaptive activities (which often are those associated with the experience of pleasure or mastery); decrease engagement in activities that maintain depression or increase risk for depression; and solve problems that limit access to reward or that maintain or increase aversive control.

Behavioral counseling: A type of therapy that seeks to change self-destructive or unhealthy behaviors.

Behavioral family therapy: A psychological approach with the premise that members of a family simultaneously influence and are influenced by each other.

Behavioral health home: A health care facility in which a person can receive both mental health and physical health care services.

Behavioral intervention: An intervention that tries to change or modify a person's actions and behaviors, through encouragement, positive and negative feedback, reward, and other techniques grounded in behavioral psychology.

Behavioral smoking cessation counseling: Counseling provided by a health care professional to assist a smoker with his or her efforts to become smoke free. Smokers who use both a smoking cessation medication in combination with behavioral counseling are more likely to quit successfully.

Benefits counseling: A service that assists people with disabilities to navigate/understand how employment or other decisions can affect benefits such as Supplemental Security Income (SSI).

Benzodiazepines ("benzos"): A class of psychotropic medications (sedatives), including diazepam (Valium®), clonazepam (Klonopin®), and lorazepam (Ativan®), used to treat anxiety and to promote sleep. They can be misused; therefore, their use is closely monitored.

Beta-blockers: A class of medication used to treat high blood pressure or a rapid heartbeat. It is sometimes used to reduce stage fright or akathisia.

Biological factors: Factors including genetic influences, brain chemistry, hormone levels, nutrition, and gender.

Biological heterogeneity: Differences at the level of biology. Biological heterogeneity is responsible for a range of treatment effects and side effects.

Bipolar depression: A depressive episode in the context of having bipolar disorder.

Bipolar disorder: The prototypical affective (mood disorder) characterized by discrete mood episodes (such as manic episode, depressive episode) with mostly normal function between mood episodes. It used to be called manic-depressive illness.

Body mass index (BMI): A number calculated by using a person's weight and height. More specifically, the BMI is a person's body mass (in kilograms) divided by the square of the body height (in meters); it can be looked up in tables or calculated using a BMI calculator. The BMI is used to determine if someone has a normal weight or is considered to have overweight or obesity.

Brain tumor: An abnormal growth or mass in the brain; not all brain tumors are cancerous. Brain tumors can represent a primary brain cancer or brain metastases (tumors that travel to the brain from other parts of the body (such as the lungs).

Brand name: The name given to a medication by the pharmaceutical company that markets the medicine. The unique name used globally that describes the chemical is called generic name or INN.

Breathing re-training: A technique which teaches slow diaphragmatic breathing to reduce anxiety.

Bupropion: A medication sold under the brand names of Wellbutrin® and Zyban® that is used to treat depression and is prescribed as a smoking-cessation aid.

Cannabis: Marijuana; a drug derived from the hemp plant. Cannabis can be smoked or eaten. One of the psychoactive ingredients in cannabis (THC, delta-9-tetrahydrocannabinol) can cause psychosis, particularly if potent cannabis products are used.

Carbamazepine (Tegretol®): One of the older antiepileptic drugs that is also used as a mood stabilizer. It leads to many side effects and can cause serious drug interactions.

Cardiologist: A medical doctor who specializes in the diagnosis and treatment of heart disease.

Cardiovascular disease: Often used interchangeably with heart disease. Cardiovascular disease involves blocked blood vessels that can cause chest pain, a heart attack, or a stroke. Other heart diseases include heart failure and arrhythmias.

Case management: A collaborative process that assesses, plans, implements, coordinates, monitors, and evaluates the options and services required to meet the client's health and human service needs.

Catatonia: A syndrome with catatonic symptoms, encompassing a wide range of psychomotor disturbances, often with too little movement or odd movements. Catatonia is associated with a variety of disorders, including mood disorders and schizophrenia.

Cells: The smallest unit of life.

Certified older adult peer specialist (COAPS): A certified peer specialist with training in supporting the needs of older adults with mental health or substance abuse challenges.

Certified peer specialist (CPS): A person with lived experience of mental illness or substance abuse challenges who is trained to support people with mental health or substance abuse challenges.

Cervical cancer screening: A test used to find changes in the cells of the cervix that could lead to cancer.

Chemist: An expert in chemistry.

Chlorpromazine (Thorazine™): The first antipsychotic used in the United States, in the early 1950s.

Chlorpromazine equivalents (CPZ-EQ): A number indicating the relative potency of an antipsychotic; it can be used to compare the dose of different antipsychotics against each other. It can help determine comparable doses when changing antipsychotics.

Cholesterol: A type of fat that is made by the liver and found in blood. You also can get cholesterol from the foods you eat. Meat, fish, eggs, butter, cheese, and milk all have cholesterol.

Chorea: A type of hyperkinetic ("too much"), abnormal movement characteristic of Huntington's disease and other conditions. Such movements involve twitching and abrupt movements of larger muscle groups in the face, trunk, and limbs.

Choreoathetosis: A type of abnormal movement, which combines chorea and athetosis (writhing movements).

Chronic kidney disease (CKD): Persistent kidney damage in which the kidneys no longer function optimally and that might worsen to the point that dialysis is needed. Common causes of CKD (also called chronic kidney failure) are hypertension and diabetes; however, lithium can also be a cause of CKD.

Chronic: In medicine, a condition that persists (as opposed to an acute condition). Most psychiatric disorders are chronic and do not disappear with treatment. Chronic problems can be managed but not cured.

Clinical interview: A meeting with a health care professional to collect information about symptoms and how they evolved, to determine a person's diagnosis and to propose treatment.

Clinical research: The study of health and disease in people, with the goal of developing better ways to prevent, diagnose, and treat medical conditions. Clinical research includes the conduct of trials in which medications are tested in people.

Clozapine (Clozaril®): The most potent antipsychotic that is also effective for treatment-resistant schizophrenia (TRS).

Clubhouse: A peer-run center for people in recovery from mental health or substance use challenges to gather information that can facilitate transitional employment, educational opportunities, and social opportunities with minimal barriers to participation.

Cognitive adaptation therapy (CAT): Services that assist people with difficulties with attention, memory, or other cognitive difficulties. The goal of these services is to minimize the effect of these difficulties on the patient's functioning through workarounds or compensation.

Community-based health center: A health center that increases access to primary care providers by virtue of being in the community near one's home.

Cognitive-behavioral therapy (CBT): A form of psychotherapy that combines cognitive therapy with behavior therapy by identifying faulty or maladaptive patterns of thinking, emotional response, or behavior and substituting them with desirable patterns of thinking, emotional responses, or behavior.

Cognitive biases: A systematic error in thinking that occurs when people are processing and interpreting information that affects their decisions and judgments.

Cognitive difficulties: Problems with remembering, learning new information, concentrating, or making decisions.

Cognitive deficits: Difficulties with brain function related to cognition.

Cognitive processing therapy (CPT): A form of cognitive-behavioral therapy originally used with victims of rape or sexual trauma and later applied to people with post-traumatic stress disorder resulting from any trauma. CPT emphasizes cognitive strategies to help people alter erroneous thinking that has emerged because of a traumatic event. For example, practitioners can work with clients on false beliefs that the world is no longer safe or that they client is incompetent because he or she "let" the traumatic event happen.

Cognitive remediation: A rehabilitation approach with the goal of restoring cognitive functioning through repeated training exercises designed to improve attention, memory, and response time.

Cognitive re-structuring: A technique used in cognitive-behavioral therapy to help the client identify his or her self-defeating beliefs or cognitive distortions and then refute and modify them so that they are adaptive and reasonable.

Cognitive symptoms: Symptoms related to cognition, such as memory difficulties, inattention, or confusion.

Collateral information: Information gathered from sources other than the patient, such as previous hospital discharge summaries or family members.

Communication skills: The ability to express oneself to others.

Community mental health centers (CMHCs): Outpatient clinics that provide comprehensive mental health services, including care for patients with serious mental illness. These centers were established to shift psychiatric care from institutions into the community.

Co-morbid: Existing simultaneously with (and usually independently of) another medical condition.

Co-morbidity: Used to describe the presence of two or more disorders at the same time. Examples are depression and social anxiety disorder, or schizophrenia and obsessive-compulsive disorder.

Competence: A person's ability to make and communicate a decision to consent to medical treatment (also called decision-making capacity).

Computed tomography (CT) scan: One of the imaging modalities that can be used to examine the brain. It is based on X-rays and is particularly good in emergencies to visualize bone injuries, like a skull fracture, or bleeding inside the brain.

Confederate: People in a research context who seem to be participants, but they are part of the research team. In cognitive-behavioral therapy, confederates are sometimes enlisted by the therapist to act in a specific role during exposure therapy.

Conspiracy websites: Websites that emphasize explanations for events that implicate conspiracy by sinister and powerful groups; often political in motivation.

Contingency management: A behavioral therapy that uses motivational incentives and tangible rewards to help a person become abstinent from drugs or alcohol.

Contingent discharge: When discharge from psychiatric services depends on meeting certain conditions prior to discharge.

Control expectancies: Factors that contribute to psychotherapy outcomes, such as the responsibility for change.

Controlled trials: A type of scientific experiment that tests the effectiveness of treatment(s) through randomly assigning study participants to a treatment group or a control group that is not treated.

Coordinated specialty care: A recovery-oriented treatment program for people with the first-episode psychosis that prioritizes shared decision-making.

Core symptoms: Those symptoms that are considered typical and characteristic of a disorder.

Core belief: Deep-seated thoughts and assumptions people hold about themselves, others, and the world.

Coronavirus: A large family of viruses that cause a range of human illness, from the common cold to COVID-19 that is responsible for the pandemic that began in 2019. Its name is derived from electron microscope pictures showing a virus with spikes that give it the appearance of a crown ("corona").

Craving: An unrelenting desire, urge, or yearning that is often a criterion for the diagnosis of a substance use disorder.

Crisis stabilization unit: An unlocked psychiatric unit designed to provide respite care for members with acute behavioral health and/or substance use disorder needs as an alternative to psychiatric hospitalization.

Crisis plan: A document that outlines the plan for a personal reaction to a crisis.

Day treatment: Programs that are often attended for a period of one or two weeks shortly after a psychiatric hospitalization that include activities and therapy offered for four to six hours per day on weekdays.

Decanoate: Shorthand for the long-acting injectable preparations of the first-generation antipsychotics, haloperidol decanoate, and fluphenazine decanoate.

Defusing: Reducing the danger or tension in a difficult situation.

Deinstitutionalization: A social movement to reduce the number of people with SMI chronically cared for in state hospitals, to care provided in the community.

Delayed sleep phase syndrome: A disorder in which a person's sleep is delayed by two hours or more beyond what is considered an acceptable or conventional bedtime. The delayed sleep then causes difficulty in being able to wake up at the desired time.

Delirium: "Acute brain failure" due to medical conditions that affect brain function. Delirious patients are confused and unable to focus or remember clearly. Delirium is reversible once the medical condition causing the delirium is successfully treated.

Delusion: A fixed and false belief that a person holds; it typically resists modification despite evidence to the contrary. It is a symptom of psychosis. Delusions are often described in terms of their theme, such as grandiose, persecutory, nihilistic, or somatic.

Delusional disorder: A psychiatric disorder with prominent delusions as the main symptom.

Delusions of persecution: One of the most common forms of delusions in which people falsely believe that they are being observed and targeted by another person or entity, like an organization, often with intent to harm them. Such delusions can become elaborate (and often bizarre) conspiracy theories.

Dementia: Disorders in which there is a cognitive decline. The most common form of dementia is Alzheimer's disease, which is a progressive disease.

Department of Child and Family (DCF): A state level organization designed to provide services to children 0 through 21 years old who are at risk or have been victims of abuse or neglect, as well as their families.

Department of Mental Health (DMH): A state mental health authority that provides access to services for people with mental health needs.

Depression: A negative affective state, ranging from unhappiness and discontent to an extreme feeling of sadness, pessimism, and despondency, and which interferes with daily life and is symptomatic of several mental health disorders. Various physical, cognitive, and social changes also tend to co-occur, including altered eating or sleeping habits, lack of energy or motivation, difficulty concentrating or making decisions, and withdrawal from social activities.

Depression and Bipolar Support Alliance (DBSA): A comprehensive, peer-run support service specifically designed for people with mood disorders and their families.

Depressive episode: A mood episode in which a person has lost the feeling of pleasure and lacks energy to accomplish things. Such episodes can stem from many causes, including medical causes, substance use, or psychiatric disorders (such as bipolar disorder, recurrent depression). If a depressive episode is severe, it is called major depressive episode (MDE) or major depressive disorder (MDD).

Deutetrabenazine (Austedo®): One of the VMAT-2 inhibitors approved for the treatment of tardive dyskinesia.

Diabetes: A condition with high blood sugar levels. Antipsychotics are a class of medications that can increase a person's risk for developing diabetes.

Diagnosis: The name of the medical or psychiatric condition that is identified as the underlying cause of a person's symptom(s). Diagnosis also refers to the process of establishing the diagnosis.

Dialectical-behavioral therapy (DBT): A therapy approach that teaches specific skills in several domains (distress tolerance, emotion regulation, and interpersonal effectiveness) to manage painful emotions and decrease conflict in relationships.

Differential diagnosis: A list of diseases that could cause a symptom or a constellation of symptoms and that need to be ruled-out before settling on the diagnosis.

Direct benefits: In the context of therapeutic or biomedical research, this refers to benefits that are the direct result of the subject's participation in the research. The benefit should be fairly immediate, and the expectation of the benefit should be well-founded scientifically.

Directly observed therapy (DOT): A specific strategy that is endorsed by the World Health Organization to improve adherence by requiring health workers, community volunteers, or family members to observe and record patients taking each dose.

Disclosure: The option to share information about a mental health diagnosis.

Discretionary trust funds: A type of trust that is set up for the benefit of one or more beneficiaries. In this particular type of trust, however, the trustee is given full discretionary authority to decide when and what funds—such as principal or income—are given to which beneficiaries.

Disease-modifying: A treatment is said to be disease-modifying if it changes for the better the natural course of the illness. Most treatments suppress symptoms but do not improve the underlying condition.

Distress intolerance: A perceived inability to fully experience unpleasant, aversive, or uncomfortable emotions, which is often accompanied by an intense desire to escape the uncomfortable emotions.

Distress tolerance skills: A person's perceived capacity to withstand negative emotional and/or other aversive states (such as physical discomfort) and the behavioral act of withstanding distressing internal states elicited by a stressor.

Diuretics: Medications designed to increase the amount of water and salt expelled from the body as urine.

Dopamine: A neurotransmitter involved in many psychiatric and neurological disorders, including schizophrenia and depression.

Dopamine agonist: A drug that activates dopamine receptors.

Dopamine antagonist: A drugs that blocks dopamine receptors. All currently available antipsychotics are dopamine antagonists, which are believed to be essential to their mechanism of action.

Dopamine blockade: The mechanism of action of antipsychotics (dopamine antagonists) that blocks dopamine receptors, thereby preventing dopamine (that the body makes) from acting on its receptor.

Dopamine receptor: A receptor in the brain that is the target of antipsychotic medications and the source of certain side effects, such as extrapyramidal symptoms.

Dopamine-2 receptor: A receptor targeted by most antipsychotic drugs.

Drop-in center: Like clubhouses, a rehabilitation facility for people in recovery to provide educational opportunities and social opportunities with minimal barriers to participation.

Dual diagnosis: A term usually used to describe both a mental illness (such as schizophrenia) and a substance use problem (such as an alcohol use disorder).

Dynamic therapy: A talking therapy that aims to reveal unconscious content of a person's psyche to alleviate tension.

Dysphoria: A mental state of profound discontent with a depressed mood.

EAGLES trial: A large, multi-center, randomized, and placebo-controlled trial that examined the safety and efficacy of varenicline, bupropion, and a transdermal nicotine patch for smoking cessation.

Early warning signs: Subtle but identifiable changes in thought, affect, and behavior that signal the onset of an episode of illness.

Early insomnia: Sleep problem characterized by difficulty in falling asleep, with an increase in sleep latency (in other words, the time between going to bed and falling asleep).

Early warning signs of relapse: Signs or symptoms that herald worsening of a psychiatric illness (such as a sleep disturbance).

Eclectic: Deriving ideas from abroad array of sources.

Electrocardiogram (ECG/EKG): A test of the electrical activity of the heart; it assesses the heart rate, rhythm, and vectors of electrical impulses in the heart.

Electroconvulsive therapy (ECT): An effective treatment for catatonia, depression, and psychosis. It requires brief anesthesia, for greater comfort during the procedure, so that an electrical current can be administered to the brain to cause a seizure. Most people are substantially better after a course of ECT (several treatments, two or three times per week, and for several weeks).

Electroencephalogram (EEG): A test of the electrical activity of the brain. Abnormal brain wave patterns are seen in epilepsy and in many other conditions that affect the brain (such as delirium).

Electroencephalography: The process of conducting an electroencephalogram.

Emotional expressivity: The *emotional* response to an event that can vary between people in terms of intensity, the speed at which it peaks, and the return from this peak to its baseline.

Emotional dysregulation: The inability of a person to control or regulate his or her emotional responses to provocative stimuli.

Emotional reactivity: The tendency to experience frequent and intense emotional arousal.

Emotional suppression: A type of emotional regulation strategy that is used to cope with uncomfortable thoughts and feelings through the conscious inhibition of these experiences.

Emotion-focused coping: A stress-management strategy in which a person focuses on regulating his or her negative emotional reactions to a stressor, rather than taking actions to change the stressor itself (as in problem-focused coping).

Employee Assistance Program (EAP): A voluntary, work-based program that offers free and confidential assessments, short-term counseling, referrals, and follow-up services to employees who have personal and/or work-related problems.

Entitlement programs: A federal program or provision of law that requires payments to any person or unit of government that meets the eligibility criteria established by law. Entitlements constitute a binding obligation on the part of the federal government, and eligible recipients have legal recourse if the obligation is not fulfilled. Social Security, veterans' compensation, and pensions are examples of entitlement programs.

Entitlements: Binding obligations of the federal government, such as Social Security.

Epidemiological research: A type of research that measures diseases and deaths in a population to understand treatment needs and causes of diseases.

Epilepsy: A neurological disorder with seizures as the core manifestation. It can be genetic or be caused by a brain injury.

Estate planning: The process of designating who will receive your assets and handle your responsibilities after your death or incapacitation.

Etiology: The cause of a disease.

Euphoria: A state of elation. It can be normal or occur in a pathological condition with an elevated mood, as in a manic episode.

Evidence-based employment: Types of programs that work with people with mental health needs to find and keep jobs. This includes developing job goals, providing assistance with the job application process, and providing ongoing support.

Evidence-based practice: The idea that practices ought to be based on scientific evidence.

Evidence-based therapy: Therapy that has been proven to be effective based on scientific research.

Expectancies: The anticipated effect of a behavior that can serve as a motivator of behavior.

Exposure therapy: A technique used in the treatment of anxiety disorders that involves repeated real, visualized, or simulated exposure to (or confrontation with) a feared situation, a feared object, or a traumatic event or memory to achieve habituation.

Extrapyramidal symptom (EPS): A general term for a group of muscular side effects, specifically from antipsychotics, including akathisia, Parkinsonism, and dystonia.

Extrinsic motivation: An external incentive to engage in a specific activity, especially motivation arising from the expectation of punishment or reward.

False positive test result: A test result that comes back as positive even though the condition is not present. False positive test results occur frequently when a test is ordered to exclude a disease that is unlikely to be present.

Family-focused therapy: A time-limited treatment consisting of psychoeducation, family communication, and problem-solving skills.

Fatty acid: A fat that is important in metabolism; it is part of our food intake. Fatty acids come in different forms, depending on their chemical structure (such as saturated fatty acids, polyunsaturated fatty acids [PUFAs], trans fats). Fatty acids combine to build triglycerides.

First-episode psychosis: The first time a person experiences psychotic symptoms or a psychotic episode.

First-generation antipsychotics (FGAs): A term for older antipsychotics that started to come on the market in the late 1950s. Of those, only haloperidol and fluphenazine are still commonly used, particularly in their long-acting injectable (LAI) form. FGAs have a relatively high risk for causing tardive dyskinesia, as compared to second-generation antipsychotics (SGAs).

First-line antipsychotic: An antipsychotic that is tried first.

Food and Drug Administration (FDA): The federal agency that, among other things, is responsible for approving medications that have been shown in clinical trials to be safe and effective.

Forensic peer specialist: Certified peer specialists who utilize their own history of criminal justice system involvement and mental health recovery to deliver services related to behavioral health and criminal justice system involvement.

Formal thought disorder: A disorder of the organization and expression of speech, in contrast to disorders of the content of speech (such as delusions, hallucinations). People with a formal thought disorder can be difficult to understand or follow. It is a core symptom of schizophrenia.

Freudian therapy: Treatment that aims to help patients better understand the unconscious forces that play a role in their current behavior, thoughts, and emotions, based on the theories of Sigmund Freud.

Fuel assistance programs: A state-provided resource that assists in covering the costs of heating bills.

Functional imaging: Brain imaging that examines the activity and function of the brain, as opposed to its structure. Examples of functional imaging modalities include fMRI (functional magnetic resonance imaging), MEG (magnetoencephalography), and PET (positron emission tomography) scans.

Functional remission: Whereas symptomatic remission refers to the disappearance of symptoms, functional remission denotes the restoration of a previous level of function (such as school function, work function).

Gabapentin (Neurontin®): An antiepileptic drug that is also used to relieve pain, anxiety, and insomnia.

Galactorrhea: A milky discharge from the nipple (unrelated to breast feeding). It can be a sign of elevated prolactin levels due to dopamine blockade from certain antipsychotics.

Generalized anxiety disorder (GAD): An anxiety disorder marked by chronic excessive anxiety and worry that is difficult to control, causes distress or impairment in daily functioning, and is accompanied by three or more associated symptoms (restlessness, irritability, poor concentration, and sleep disturbances).

Generic: Drugs that are copies of brand name drugs. They are chemically identical and should be interchangeable (but they might look different).

Genetic: Relating to genes or heredity.

Genetics: The study of genes and how the qualities of parents are given to their children by the parents' genes.

Global disease burden: The impact of a disease on societies, as measured in cost, disability, and mortality. Serious mental illnesses (SMIs) have a high disease burden.

Glycine: An amino acid that is also a neurotransmitter. It is available as a supplement and is under investigation as a treatment for schizophrenia, among other disorders. It targets the NMDA receptor.

Gold standard: In medicine, the diagnostic test or treatment that is considered the best for a condition and against which other tests or treatment are measured.

Grief: Sorrow and sadness due to a loss, especially from the death of a loved one.

Group home: A living arrangement for people with a SMI; it often includes supervision and management. Some group homes are run by the state; others are private.

Guardian: A person entrusted by the law with the care of the person, property, or both of another who is legally incapable of managing his or her own affairs.

Guardianship: The position of being legally responsible for the care of someone who is unable to manage his or her own affairs.

Half-life (t ½): The time it takes for half of a drug that has been administered to be excreted (specifically, the elimination half-life). It takes about four half-lives before a drug is completely gone from the body. The half-life determines how often a drug must be taken.

Hallucination: The perception of something that is not present. This can occur in any of the senses, such as hearing a voice (auditory hallucinations), feeling something (tactile hallucinations), smelling something (olfactory hallucinations), tasting something (gustatory hallucinations), or seeing something (visual hallucinations). Hallucinations are examples of psychosis.

Haloperidol (Haldol®): A high-potency, first-generation antipsychotic. One of the first antipsychotics, it is still widely used. It carries a high risk of TD.

Health care proxy: A document that names someone you trust as your proxy, or agent, to express your wishes and make health care decisions for you if you are unable to speak for yourself.

Health care agent: A person you choose in advance to make health care decisions for you if you become unable to do so.

Health inequities: Differences in health status or in the distribution of health resources between different population groups that arise from the social conditions in which people are born, grow, live, work, and age.

Healthy controls: In clinical research, a healthy group of people who serves as a comparison group.

Heart attack: A condition in which a part of the heart muscle doesn't get enough blood. Also called myocardial infarction.

Heart disease: One of several types of heart conditions, the most common of which is coronary artery disease (CAD), which interferes with the blood flow to the heart and can cause a heart attack.

Hope kit: A personally meaningful collection of objects designed to serve as a coping tool for suicidal thinking.

Huntington's disease: A progressive neurological disorder with characteristic involuntary movements (chorea). It also presents with disturbances of mood and cognition.

Hypercholesterolemia: High cholesterol in the blood stream. It can be diagnosed with a blood test. It is a risk factor for heart attacks and strokes. There are several types of cholesterol, with so-called HDL cholesterol ("good cholesterol) being protective.

Hypertension: High blood pressure.

Hypnotic: A so-called sleeping pill; a class of medicines used to manage insomnia.

Hypomania: A mild form of mania in which people are energetic, talkative, and full of ideas and plans. It differs from mania where the frenzied state precludes organized action. Hypomanic people can be quite productive. Some people are temperamentally hypomanic (hyperthymic temperament).

Hypothyroidism: Low function of the thyroid gland. Symptoms include fatigue, weight gain, and dry skin.

Iatrogenic: A problem inadvertently caused by a physician while diagnosing or treating a patient.

Idiosyncratic: An uncommon and unpredictable side effect; it is probably because of genetic factors or an unusual immune response.

Illness management: A process to oversee and manage illnesses and conditions.

Illness self-management: The ability of the person, in conjunction with family, community, and health care professionals, to manage symptoms, treatments, lifestyle changes, and psychosocial, cultural, and spiritual consequences of health conditions.

Impaired reality testing: Psychosis is often defined as having impaired reality testing, which means a person is not able to perceive reality correctly. It manifests as having delusions or experiencing hallucinations.

Incidence: The occurrence of new cases of disease or injury in a population over a specified period. Although some epidemiologists use incidence to mean the number of new cases in a community, others use incidence to mean the number of new cases per unit of population.

Individual placement and support: A model of supported employment for people with serious mental illnesses.

Informed consent: An important tenet in medicine that requires voluntary agreement to treatment before it can be given because the patient believes it makes sense for him or her. A patient needs to be given enough understandable information to come to an informed decision regarding the proposed treatment.

Inpatient treatment: Psychiatric care that takes place in a hospital setting and includes close monitoring.

Inpatient: Being a hospitalized patient. For some procedures and for some treatments, an inpatient admission is necessary, particularly when close monitoring is required.

Insight-oriented: Treatment aimed at providing awareness of your unconscious mental life to reduce distress.

Insight: The capacity to gain an accurate and deep intuitive understanding of a person or thing.

Insomnia: A sleep disorder in which a person has difficulties falling asleep or staying asleep. Insomnia is called chronic insomnia if it lasts for more than one month. Insomnia can stem from a wide variety of causes, including poor sleep habits (sleep hygiene), drug or alcohol use, or depression/anxiety.

Institutional review board (IRB): An appropriately constituted group that has been formally designated to review and monitor biomedical research involving human subjects.

Institutionalization: Being placed for longer periods in an institution, such as a state hospital or prison.

Integrated care: A general term for any attempt to fully or partially blend behavioral health services with general and/or specialty medical services.

Intelligence tests: One of a variety of tests employed to assess a person's intelligence. This includes tests to calculate a person's intelligence quotient (IQ).

Intensive outpatient program (IOP): A typical IOP program offers up to 30 hours a week of group therapy for behavioral health or addiction treatment. An IOP allows the person to be able to participate in their daily affairs, such as work, and then participate in treatment at an appropriate facility in the morning or at the end of the day.

Inter-family communication: Discussions occurring among multiple family members.

Internalized stigma: The absorbed negative messages or stereotypes about mental illness that refer to oneself.

International non-proprietary name (INN): The official and unique name of a medication that is the same in all countries. When a drug is sold in a pharmacy, companies often give it a brand name that is different from the INN and that is usually different in each country. A non-proprietary name is also called a generic name.

Interoceptive exposure: A cognitive-behavioral therapy technique used in the treatment of panic disorder that involves exposure to feared bodily sensations.

Interpersonal effectiveness: The ability to interact with others and a primary focus of DBT.

Interpersonal social rhythm therapy: A treatment designed to help people improve their mood by understanding their biological and social rhythms.

Interpersonal therapy (IPT): A time-limited and evidence-based approach developed to treat mood disorders whose main goal is to improve the quality of a client's interpersonal relationships and social functioning to help reduce their distress.

Intrinsic motivation: An incentive to engage in a specific activity that derives from pleasure in the activity itself, rather than because of any external benefits that might be obtained.

Job development: When an employment specialist contacts employers in the community to identify a job that matches the preferences and interests of a specific person.

Labile: Easily altered.

Lamotrigine (Lamictal®): An anti-epileptic drug that is also used as a mood stabilizer.

Late insomnia: Difficulty with early morning awakenings in the absence of initial or middle insomnia (also referred to as terminal insomnia or sleep-offset insomnia).

LEAP method (Listen, Empathize, Agree, Partner): An approach for communicating with people affected by mental illness with poor insight that was developed by Dr. Xavier Amador.

Level of care: The amount or degree of support and intensity of treatment offered for psychiatric conditions.

Licensed independent clinical social worker (LICSW): A trained social worker who helps clients with mental health issues.

Licensed mental health counselor (LMHC): A mental health professional who works with people to improve mental well-being.

Limited release of medical information: A legal document in which a person identifies the specific pieces of protected health information that he or she permits sharing with others, such as a family member.

Lipid: An organic compound, such as a fatty acid. Lipids are components of cells.

Lithium toxicity: Lithium is a drug with a narrow therapeutic index; it causes tremor, diarrhea, and confusion when the blood level is too high.

Lithium: A first-line treatment for bipolar disorder.

L-methyl folate: The biologically active form of the vitamin folate.

Loneliness: Increasingly recognized as a public health problem, loneliness is the subjective and distressing feeling of having too few or no meaningful relationships.

Long-acting injectable (LAI): An antipsychotic that can be given as an intramuscular or subcutaneous injection, usually every two to four weeks, depending on the medication. It is often a good alternative to taking a pill by mouth every day.

Magnetic resonance imaging (MRI) scan: A test of brain imaging that uses strong magnetic fields, without exposing people to X-rays to provide detailed pictures of the brain's structure (gray and white matter).

Magnification bias: The tendency to pay more attention to negative events and experiences than positive ones.

Maintenance: Long-term treatment to prevent relapse.

Maintenance treatment: Treatment to keep a condition from returning.

Major tranquilizer: An old term for an antipsychotic.

Mammogram: An X-ray of the breast used to detect early signs of breast cancer.

Mania: A state with abnormally elevated mood, accelerated thinking, overactivity, and little sleep. Mania is a core feature of bipolar disorder (manic-depressive illness) but manic episodes can also occur in other circumstances (such as with administration of steroids).

Manic: A description for a person who is in a manic episode. A manic person speaks rapidly will be difficult to interrupt, might have many unrealistic plans, and be full of energy, seemingly without the need for sleep.

Manic-depressive illness: The old term for bipolar disorder, the prototypical mood disorder characterized by discrete mood episodes (such as manic or depressive episode) and mostly normal function between mood episodes.

Manualized therapies: Interventions performed according to a specific guideline to maximize consistent therapy.

Mechanism of action (MOA): A term for how a medication produces its effects. The MOA of psychiatric medications often involves blocking or activating specific receptors in the brain that then leads to changes in neural networks.

Medicaid: A federal and state program that helps with medical costs for people with limited resources or income.

Meditation: A technique to increase mindfulness.

Mens sana in corpora sano: An old Latin adage (attributed to the Roman poet Juvenal) that translates as, "A healthy mind in a healthy body." It emphasizes that mind and body are connected and that psychological well-being requires physical health (and vice versa).

Mental status examination (MSE): The examination of a person's mental state, corresponding to the physical exam in medicine. It includes an assessment of a person's appearance, behavior, ability to think, and the content of their thinking (including psychosis), cognition, mood (including suicidal ideation), and insight and judgment.

Metabolic syndrome: A constellation of conditions (high blood pressure, high blood sugar, excess fat around the waist, and abnormal cholesterol levels) that increase a person's risk for cardiovascular disease and stroke. Antipsychotics increase the risk for the metabolic syndrome, in part because of weight gain.

Metabolism: The chemical processes in an organism that sustain life (such as converting food into energy, which produces energy for the cells).

Metacognition: Awareness and understanding of one's own thought processes.

Metformin: A first-line medication to treat type 2 diabetes. It is also used as an add-on strategy to prevent diabetes induced by antipsychotics.

Microbiome: A term for all the microbes, particularly their genetic material, that are inside a person's gut.

Microbiota: All the microorganisms of a given site.

Middle insomnia: Difficulty maintaining sleep in the absence of initial or late insomnia (also referred to as sleep maintenance insomnia).

Migraine: A specific type of headache that is recurrent and is often accompanied by nausea and visual disturbances.

Mindfulness-based strategies: Strategies to focus on the present in a way that is non-judgmental.

Mindfulness: The practice of maintaining a state of heightened or complete awareness of one's thoughts, emotions, or present-moment experiences without judging or reacting to them.

Mobile crisis service: A rapid response service that responds to problems outside of hospital settings.

Mobile phone subsidies: A government-funded program that covers part or all the cost of cellphones for customers.

Mobile application: Most commonly referred to as an "app," a mobile application is a type of software designed to run on a mobile device, such as a smartphone or tablet computer.

Mood stabilizers: A class of medications used for the treatment of bipolar disorder. Mood stabilizers treat acute mood episodes (mania and depression) and are sometimes effective as maintenance treatment to prevent the recurrence of a mood episode. Mood stabilizers include lithium, many antipsychotics, and several antiepileptic drugs.

Morbidity: A term that refers to having a medical problem. It is often applied to populations.

Mortality: Refers to dying or being dead.

Motivation: The impetus that gives purpose or direction to behavior.

Motor symptoms: Symptoms (such as muscle stiffness, tremor, or abnormal movements) related to disorders of movement, like Parkinson's disease, or tardive dyskinesia.

Multi-family group therapy: A typical family therapy that integrates psychoeducation and behavioral family therapy into a multiple family group format.

Multiple sclerosis (MS): A major neurological disorder that damages the white matter of the nervous system (the fibers that connect nerve cells) and that can result in significant disability and death. It is the result of an autoimmune process that attacks and destroys nerve fibers (myelin).

Myocardial infarction (MI): A heart attack, usually because of a blood clot that blocks blood flowing to heart muscle.

Myocarditis: Inflammation of the heart. It is a rare side effect of the antipsychotic clozapine.

Narcolepsy: A disorder marked by excessive daytime sleepiness, uncontrollable sleep attacks, and cataplexy (a sudden loss of muscle tone that can last up to half an hour).

National Association for Mental Illness (NAMI): A nation-wide mental health organization dedicated to building better lives for people and families affected by mental illness through education, support, and advocacy.

National Alliance for Mental Illness (NAMI) Family-to-Family: A nationwide mental health organization dedicated to using education, support, and advocacy to build better lives for people and families who are affected by mental illness.

National Institute on Disability and Independent Living and Rehabilitation Research (NIDILRR): The federal government's primary disability research agency that funds research to support the goals of community integration for people affected by disabilities.

Natural course of disease: The unfolding of a disease without treatment.

Negative symptoms: Apparent in some forms of schizophrenia, negative symptoms are characterized by deficits in social interest and motivation, as well as emotional expressivity.

Negative automatic thought: Instantaneous, habitual, and non-conscious thoughts that adversely affect a person's mood and actions. Helping people to become aware of the presence and effects of negative automatic thoughts and then testing their validity is a central task of cognitive-behavioral therapy.

Neural networks: Also referred to as brain circuits, these are brain regions that are connected and work together to support brain function. Many neurological and psychiatric disorders cause symptoms because neural networks are functioning improperly.

Neurobiological problem: Problems related to the nervous system and brain function.

Neurobiology: A branch of biology that studies the structure and function of the nervous system, which includes the brain, spinal cord, and peripheral nerves.

Neurocognitive testing: Testing that emphasizes cognitive aspects of brain function, such as attention and memory.

Neurodevelopment: The manner in which the brain forms. Neurodevelopmental disorders are those disorders where brain development goes awry. Many chronic psychiatric disorders are thought to be rooted in neurodevelopmental disturbances.

Neurolepsis: Slowed movements (psychomotor retardation) associated with use of dopamine-blocking antipsychotics.

Neuroleptic: An old term for an antipsychotic.

Neurologic: Related to problems affecting the nervous system.

Neurological deficit: Abnormal function of a body area due to impairment of the brain, spinal cord, or nerves.

Neurology: A branch of medicine that concerns itself with the study and treatment of diseases of the nervous system (brain and spinal cord).

Neuropsychiatric disorders: Disorders that are firmly grounded in diseases of the nervous system. Neuropsychiatrists focus on the brain as an organ and how brain diseases lead to psychiatric symptoms (such as the psychiatric problems that occur in epilepsy or multiple sclerosis). The work of a neuropsychiatrists overlaps with those of neurologists.

Neuropsychologist: A psychologist who specializes in understanding brain-behavior relationships, particularly those related to cognitive functions, such as learning, attention, memory, and executive functions.

Neuroscience-based nomenclature (NbN): A classification and naming of drugs based on their pharmacological action, particularly their mechanisms of action.

Nicotine gum: A short-acting medication used as a smoking cessation aid, which decreases craving and other withdrawal symptoms by providing nicotine. Nicotine gum is available by prescription or over the counter. Can be used in combination with a nicotine patch.

Nicotine lozenge: A short-acting medication used as a smoking-cessation aid, which decreases craving and other withdrawal symptoms by providing nicotine. Nicotine lozenges are available by prescription or over the counter. Can be used in combination with a nicotine patch.

Nicotine patch: A long-acting (24-hour) medication used as smoking-cessation aid. Nicotine patches are available by prescription or over the counter. Can be used in combination with any short-acting form of nicotine replacement.

N-methyl-D-aspartate (NMDA) receptor: A type of receptor in the brain that is involved in many neurological and psychiatric disorders.

Nomenclature: The official names and terms used in science, such as a book of plant names or psychiatric disorders. A nomenclature is a classification system.

Non-adherence: Not following treatment recommendations. This term usually implies that medications are not being taken as prescribed or not being taken at all.

Non-biological factors: Factors that affect a disease (such as environmental, psychological, or social factors).

Non-communicable disease: Diseases that are not transmitted from person to person, like cancer or most chronic conditions (such as heart disease and diabetes).

Non-pharmacological: Not related to medications.

Non-suicidal self-injury: The deliberate, self-inflicted destruction of body tissue without suicidal intent and for purposes not socially sanctioned, including behaviors such as cutting, burning, biting, and scratching skin.

Nurse practitioner (NP): A registered nurse who had additional training that allows him or her to practice medicine (including prescribing medications) without the direct supervision of a physician.

Nutritionist: A person who studies nutrition or is an expert in nutrition.

Nystagmus: A type of repetitive and fast eye movement. It can be a sign of a disorder or of a drug side effect.

Obesity: A disorder defined by a body mass index of 30 or higher (weight in kilograms divided by height in meters squared).

Obsessive-compulsive disorder (OCD): A psychological disorder characterized by recurrent obsessions or compulsions (or both) that cause significant distress and are time-consuming or interfere with normal daily functioning.

Occupational therapists: Health care professionals who seek to optimize function of meaningful activities.

Occupational therapy (OT): A form of therapy that encourages rehabilitation through performance of activities required in daily life.

Oculogyric crisis: Involuntary movements of the eyeballs, usually looking upward where the eyes can stay fixed. It can be an acute side effect of antipsychotics that arises shortly after they are started.

Olanzapine (Zyprexa®): An effective second-generation antipsychotic, but it conveys a high risk of metabolic dysfunction.

Omega-3 fatty acid: A type of fat that is involved in many biological processes, including inflammation. While it is often taken as a supplement for a wide range of conditions such as heart disease, the benefit for most people is not proven.

Opiate: A drug that contains or is derived from opium that acts to block pain, induce sedation or sleep, depress respiration, and produce calmness or euphoria and that is associated with physiological tolerance, physical and psychological dependence, and addiction upon repeated or prolonged use.

Oral hygiene: The practice of keeping the mouth clean and healthy by brushing and flossing to prevent tooth decay and gum disease.

Organ system: A group of organs that function together. Examples include the nervous and the cardiovascular systems.

Organic: An older term indicating that there is a physical or biochemical change that can be detected with a medical test. In psychiatry, many conditions are non-organic (functional) as no abnormality can be detected with the usual tests. The term organic, however, is no longer used as all psychiatric disorders have an "organic" (brain-based) basis.

Osteoporosis: A disease in which the bones become more porous and brittle, making them easier to break.

Out-of-pocket: A payment option for psychiatric services that comes directly from the client.

Outpatient: Medical care that is provided outside of a hospital, as in an office or clinic.

Outpatient commitment: A civil court procedure wherein a legal process orders a person diagnosed with a severe mental disorder to adhere to an outpatient treatment plan.

Outpatient treatment: A psychiatric treatment option that is office-based.

Outreach workers: Mental health workers who provide direct support and assist people with navigating and connecting to rehabilitation services in their local areas, often provided by state agencies or mental health agencies.

Overnight sleep study: A non-invasive test that involves spending the night at a sleep laboratory; it is performed to diagnose sleep disorders, such as sleep apnea, insomnia, and restless legs syndrome. Today, sleep studies can often be done at a person's home.

Package insert: The official material that summarizes the safety and efficacy of a medication, based on the materials submitted to the FDA by the pharmaceutical company for drug approval. It includes medications side effects observed in clinical trials.

Pandemic: An infectious disease outbreak that has spread over many countries and continents; it can be worldwide.

Panic disorder: An anxiety disorder characterized by recurrent unexpected panic attacks followed by a month or more of worry about their recurrence, implications, or consequences or that is characterized by a change in behavior related to the panic attacks.

Paranoia: Being mistrustful and suspicious without justification.

Parkinson's disease: A progressive disease of dopamine neurons in the basal ganglia that causes a movement disorder, as well as affective, behavioral, and cognitive symptoms. Symptoms include tremor (shaking), rigidity (muscle stiffness), and bradykinesia (slow movements) which results in a characteristic shuffling, slow gait with no arm swing and a tremor at rest.

Parkinsonian: Appearing as though someone has Parkinson's disease.

Parkinsonism: Motor side effects of antipsychotics that mimic Parkinson's disease.

Partial hospital program: A type of program available to treat mental illness or substance abuse that involves the patient living at home and who typically goes to the treatment center 5–6 hours a day, Monday–Friday.

Partial hospitalization program: A type of program used to treat mental illness and/or substance abuse. The patient lives at home and commutes to the program daily to participate in group therapy and psychopharmacology appointments.

Passive GPS data collection: Collection of movement data using a mobile phone.

Pathognomonic: A sign or symptom that points to a very specific disease, which helps to make a diagnosis.

Pathophysiology: The abnormal physiology that underlies a disease.

Patient Health Questionnaire-9 (PHQ-9): An instrument designed to screen for depression in primary care settings.

Patient-centered care: Care that is organized around a patient and in a partnership between a physician and patient. Such care accounts for individual patient preferences, needs, and values as a guiding principle for treatment decisions.

Pedometer: An instrument for estimating the distance traveled on foot by recording the number of steps taken.

Peer support: Help and support from others with lived experience that is provided to people with a psychiatric or substance use disorder. Peer support can help with recovery.

Peer specialist: A person with a lived experience of mental illness or substance abuse challenges who is trained to support people with ongoing mental health or substance abuse challenges.

Persecutory delusions: Unfounded beliefs that one is being persecuted despite a lack of evidence.

Person-centered therapy: *See* person-centered care.

Personality test: A group of tests to measure human personality constructs. They can be objective tests (such as the Minnesota Multiphasic Personality Inventory [MMPI]) or projective tests (like the Rorschach test).

Person-centered care: Similar to patient-centered care but with an even greater emphasis on patients as individuals.

Pharmacologic profile: The characteristics of a drug, its efficacy, and its side effects; including how it acts biologically; how it is absorbed, metabolized, and excreted.

Pharmacotherapy: Medical treatment by means of drugs.

Phobic: Having or involving an extreme or irrational fear of (or aversion to) something.

Physical therapy (PT): Treatment of disease or injury by physical methods, such as massage and exercise.

Physiology: The study of physical and chemical processes in living organisms.

Place and train model: A model of vocational rehabilitation in which a person is placed in a job and then receives training.

Placebo: A sugar pill used in clinical research. In a typical medication study, one group of people receives the study medications, while the other receives the placebo.

Polypharmacy: The use of several medications at the same time. While polypharmacy can be rational (for example, it used for good reasons), the term is usually used critically.

Positive symptoms: A term for the characteristic symptoms of schizophrenia, specifically psychosis and hallucinations. Positive symptoms, when there is a "too much of something" are contrasted with negative symptoms, when there is something missing (such as motivation and drive).

Positive psychology: A field of psychological theory and research that focuses on the psychological states (such as contentment and joy), personal traits or character strengths (such as intimacy, integrity, altruism, and wisdom), and social institutions that enhance subjective wellbeing and make life worth living.

Positron emission tomography (PET) scan: A functional brain imaging test. It is based on radioactivity and can be used to examine biological processes in the brain, including inflammation. Clinically, it is used for the detection of small cancers and neurological disorders. Currently, PET imaging is not routinely used in psychiatry.

Post-traumatic stress disorder (PTSD): A mental disorder that can develop after a person experiences or witnesses a traumatic event. Symptoms include avoidance of reminders of the traumatic event, hyperarousal, re-experiencing (meaning flashbacks), and disturbances in thinking and mood that interfere with functioning and last for more than a month following the traumatic event.

Preference-sensitive decision: A situation in medicine where the choice between treatment options depends on a person's assessment of risks and benefits as no option is clearly the best. This situation lends itself to shared decision-making.

Present-centered: A form of focusing derived from meditative practice (from the Zen tradition) in which one is instructed to bring attention back to the present each time it wanders from the breath.

Prevention: Actions taken to avoid a disease from developing (primary prevention), to discover a disease early so that treatment is easier (secondary prevention), or to mitigate the effects of a disease and prevent its worsening (tertiary prevention).

Primary psychosis: Psychosis that is not the result of organic factors but the result of a psychiatric illness. By contrast, secondary psychosis is the result of identifiable organic factors, like a medical condition or substance use.

Primary care physician (PCP): A health care professional who practices general medicine.

Private pay: A payment option for psychiatric services that comes directly from the client, rather than being covered by health insurance.

Private residential setting: A living environment in which people receive rehabilitation support and coordinated treatment that is funded through private pay.

Pro re nata (prn): Latin abbreviation and phrase meaning, "as needed." Used for taking medications only intermittently when needed for a symptom, as opposed to being scheduled with a given frequency or at a specific time each day.

Probiotic: A preparation of live microorganisms (usually bacteria, like the bacterium lactobacillus acidophilus) taken with the idea of strengthening "good" microbes in the gut flora that can help certain medical conditions related to a disturbance of the gut flora.

Problem-focused coping: A stress-management strategy in which a person directly confronts a stressor to decrease or eliminate it.

Problem-solving skills training: Training to think differently about situations and behave differently.

Problem-solving therapy: A psychological treatment focused on managing stressors by generating possible solutions to a problem, evaluating the pros and cons of each solution, and determining a course of action based on this analysis.

Prodrome: The early period as an illness begins, before an illness is fully present. Symptoms during the prodrome are nonspecific and their significance often only becomes obvious in hindsight.

Prognosis: The probable outcome or course of a medical condition.

Program of Assertive Community Treatment (PACT): A form of community-based mental health care for people experiencing serious mental illness that interferes with their ability to live in the community, attend appointments with professionals in clinics and hospitals, and manage mental health symptoms. (See also ACT.)

Progressive muscle relaxation: A non-pharmacological method of deep muscle relaxation that involves tensing and releasing each muscle group.

Projective tests: A type of personality test (like the Rorschach ink blots) in which people must respond to ambiguous stimuli that are thought to reveal hidden motivations or thoughts.

Prolactin: A hormone secreted by the pituitary gland and important for producing breast milk after giving birth. Some antipsychotics increase prolactin in the blood stream, which can lead to characteristic side effects (sexual side effects, milk excretion, or breast growth).

Prolactin-sparing antipsychotics: Those antipsychotics that do not increase prolactin levels. This includes most antipsychotics except first-generation antipsychotics and risperidone and paliperidone that increase prolactin levels.

Prostate exam: An exam performed by a doctor that can identify an inflamed prostate or signs of prostate cancer.

Pseudo-refractoriness: The mistaken appearance of being treatment-resistant or treatment-refractory. A common reason is medication non-adherence.

Psychiatric nurse practitioner: A medical practitioner who has a registered nursing license, completed an accredited graduate-level program, passed a national certification exam, and earned an advanced practice nurse practitioner license in the state in which they practice.

Psychiatric (or psychosocial) rehabilitation: A set of practices that is intended to be used in conjunction with psychiatric treatment and therapy. The goal is to optimize functioning and wellbeing by strengthening remediating or compensating (to the extent possible) for deficits that were affected by serious mental illness (SMI).

Psychiatric advance directive: A legal document that details your preferences for future mental health treatment, services, and supports or that names another person to make treatment decisions if you are in a crisis and unable to make decisions.

Psychiatrist: A medical doctor who, after finishing medical school, specializes in the diagnosis and treatment of mental illnesses.

Psychoanalysis: A system of psychological theory and therapy to treat mental disorders by investigating the interaction of conscious and unconscious elements through free association.

Psychodynamic therapy: A technique involving the interpretation of mental and emotional processes to reduce distress.

Psychodynamically-oriented therapy: Treatment that examines relationships in the context of unconscious processes.

Psychoeducation: An evidence-based therapeutic intervention that provides information and support to cope with illness.

Psychological symptoms: Symptoms that affect emotions, thoughts, or related behaviors.

Psychological therapies: Talking therapies to understand your feelings.

Psychologist: An expert or specialist in psychology who often provides therapy and counseling services.

Psychopathology: The study of mental disorders and abnormal behaviors. It is also known as abnormal psychology.

Psychophysiological insomnia: A state of heightened arousal and learned sleep-preventing association that precludes sleep and causes impaired functioning during wakefulness. The insomnia must be present for at least one month.

Psychosis: Impaired reality testing. The presence of certain symptoms (delusions or hallucinations) is considered evidence that impaired reality testing is present.

Psychosocial rehabilitation: A discipline that tries to mitigate the effects of having a SMI, with emphasis on returning to function (such as school or work) despite having a psychiatric illness.

Psychosocial toxicity: Complications from having a psychiatric illness that affect your social life, such as losing a job or gaining a bad reputation.

Psychotherapy: The use of psychological methods in talk therapy.

Psychotic depression: Depression with psychotic symptoms.

Psychotic disorder: Abnormal function of the mind that results in difficulty determining what is real and what is not real.

Psychotic symptom: In its most narrow definition, psychotic symptoms include delusions or hallucinations. Sometimes, a formal thought disorder and catatonia are included.

Psychotic: Relating to, denoting, or suffering from psychotic symptoms (such as hallucinations or delusions).

Psychotropic: A broad term for a drug that acts on the mind and affects a person's mental state. Such drugs can change thinking, mood, and behavior. Psychotropic medications are used to treat psychiatric symptoms and disorders.

Quality of life (QOL): A person's overall wellbeing and happiness. Improving QOL is an important treatment and rehabilitation target.

Quetiapine (Seroquel®): A second-generation antipsychotic that is also used in the treatment of mood disorders.

Quo ad vitam: A Latin phrase to mean, "with regard to life." It is usually used together with prognosis, as in "a person's prognosis quo ad vitam."

Randomized controlled trial (RCT): A type of scientific experiment that tests effectiveness of treatment(s) through randomly assigning study participants to treatment or control groups. (People in control groups are not treated.)

Receptor profile: Refers to the number and types of receptors in the brain that a psychiatric medication targets. The receptor profile of a drug can explain some side effects.

Recovery Learning Community (RLC): Consumer-run networks of self-help, peer support, information sharing, and advocacy services for people with serious mental illness.

Recovery: In medicine, this term is often used to mean a return to a normal state of health. In psychiatry, where most conditions are chronic, this term is usually used to indicate psychological well-being and managing life even if the condition is still present.

Recovery coach: A person with some foundation in his or her own recovery from addiction who uses personal experience to help and support others in their recoveries.

Recovery-oriented cognitive behavioral therapy: A treatment approach that promotes strengths-based recovery utilizing an individual's own interests, values, and aspirations in life.

Recovery skills training: A process to learn how to support long-term recovery from substance use.

Refractory: Refers to a disease that does not respond to treatment. The disease is then called treatment-resistant or treatment-refractory.

Refusal skills: A set of methods and strategies for saying "no" that are designed to help people avoid high-risk situations for substance use.

Rehabilitation: A branch of medicine that works on restoring a person's function that has been lost because of an illness, with an emphasis on improving a person's quality of life.

Relapse: The return (recurrence) of a condition that was successfully treated, without symptoms. It can be applied to mood episodes, psychotic episodes, and to substance use disorders.

Relaxation training: Any method, process, procedure, or activity that helps a person to relax or reduce levels of pain, anxiety, stress or anger.

Remission: The reduction (partial remission) or complete disappearance (full remission) of signs and symptoms of a disease. Remission is usually applied to symptoms (symptomatic remission) but it can also be applied to function (functional remission).

Renal: Relating to the kidneys.

Representative payee: A person or an organization appointed to receive Social Security benefits for a person who can't manage or direct the management of his or her benefits. Representative payees are required to provide detailed accounting reports of how benefits were dispersed.

Residential program: A program that provides 24-hour care and services to people who need a less-structured environment than that of an inpatient program and who are capable of self-preservation in the event of an emergency in the organization.

Resilience: The capacity to recover from difficulties.

Respiratory disease: Respiratory diseases include asthma, chronic obstructive pulmonary disease (COPD), pulmonary fibrosis, pneumonia, and lung cancer. Also called a lung disorder or pulmonary disease.

Restitutio ad integrum: Latin for "restoration of full health"; it is used to describe a treatment goal.

Reverse integrated care: A system of care that embeds primary care practitioners in mental health settings, where people with SMIs are more likely to present for treatment.

Reward value: The positive value that a person ascribes to an object, behavioral act, or an internal physical state.

Risk factor: A variable associated with an increased risk of a disease or condition.

Risperidone (Risperdal®): A widely used second-generation antipsychotic with a good balance between efficacy and side effects.

Salutogenesis: A medical approach that focuses on the sources of health as opposed to the origins of disease. It examines factors like coping or resilience that support health and wellbeing.

Safety behavior: Actions taken to avoid, prevent, or manage a potential threat.

Sarcosine: An amino acid that occurs naturally in the body but has also been tested as a treatment of schizophrenia. It targets the NDMA receptor.

Schizophrenia: The prototypical psychotic disorder with prominent and persistent psychotic symptoms in addition to other symptoms (such as negative symptoms, or cognitive symptoms).

Schizoaffective disorder: One of the schizophrenia spectrum disorders with admixtures of mood symptoms and psychotic symptoms.

Schizophrenia spectrum disorders: An umbrella term for a group of psychotic disorders that share clinical features and likely a neurobiology. Disorders usually included are schizophrenia, schizoaffective disorder, delusional disorder, and schizotypal disorder.

Schizophreniform disorder: A "schizophrenia-like" disorder that looks like schizophrenia but does not persist beyond six months.

Schizotypal disorder: One of the schizophrenia-spectrum disorder, with attenuated psychotic symptoms (such as ideas of reference, odd beliefs, and suspiciousness) and difficulties establishing close relationships. It resembles schizophrenia and is sometimes considered a personality disorder.

Secondary psychosis: Psychosis that is the result of organic factors, such as a medical illness or substance use.

Second-generation antipsychotic (SGA): A general term for antipsychotics that have fewer motor side effects compared to the older, first-generation antipsychotics. While they are roughly equally effective (with the exception of clozapine), they vary widely in their side effect profiles.

Sedative-hypnotic: A class of medications to improve anxiety and for sleep. Included are benzodiazepines and some sleep medications (the "Z-drugs," such as zolpidem).

Sedentary behavior: Any waking behavior characterized by low energy expenditure (such as sitting or lying down).

Seizure disorder: A neurological disorder, such as epilepsy, in which seizures are the core feature.

Seizure: A sudden and pathological electric discharge in the brain that can cause a variety of symptoms, depending on where the electric discharge occurs. For example, seizures cause convulsions if the motor area of the brain is affected.

Selective serotonin re-uptake inhibitor (SSRI): A class of medications that block the serotonin transporter as their main mechanisms of action. SSRIs are used for depression and anxiety disorders.

Self-compassion: Extending caring, kindness, and acceptance to oneself in instances of perceived inadequacy, failure, or general suffering.

Self-management: The ability of the person, in conjunction with family, community, and health care professionals, to manage symptoms, treatments, lifestyle changes, and psychosocial, cultural, and spiritual consequences of health conditions.

Self-Management and Recovery Training (SMART Recovery): An international nonprofit organization that assists people seeking to abstain from addiction using a secular- and science-based approach that incorporates cognitive-behavioral therapy and non-confrontational motivational methods.

Self-stigma: The internalization of negative attitudes about illness or behaviors.

Serious mental illness (SMI): Any psychiatric disorder that affects a person's life and that requires long-term treatment. The main disorders in this category are schizophrenia, bipolar disorder, and severe forms of depression.

Serotonin: A brain neurotransmitter.

Serotonin transporter: The target of many medications, particularly antidepressants. The serotonin transporter removes serotonin from the synaptic cleft and shuttles it back into neurons for reuse.

Serotonin-norepinephrine re-uptake inhibitor (SNRI): A class of antidepressants that inhibits the re-uptake of serotonin and norepinephrine as their mechanisms of action.

Shared decision-making (SDM): A philosophy of treatment in medicine that respects patient autonomy and tries to help patients make informed decisions about their treatment. In this model, physicians provide treatment options and information and then help the patient weigh the information and come to the best decision for his or her specific situation and preferences.

Shotgun approach: A term used for a diagnostic medical work-up in which many tests are ordered, somewhat indiscriminately. Aside from cost, this approach is fraught with difficulties, particularly false-positive results.

Sialorrhea: The medical term for drooling. It can be a medication side effect, particularly from antipsychotics (Parkinsonism and clozapine-associated sialorrhea). It is sometimes also called "hypersalivation."

Sign: An objective, observable indication of a disorder or disease.

Sleep apnea: A condition in which breathing stops for at least 10 seconds during sleep and that is commonly associated with daytime sleepiness.

Sleep disorder: A disorder of sleep patterns that can be severe enough to interfere with a person's normal physical, mental, and emotional functioning.

Sleep hygiene: Habits and environments that are conducive to good quality sleep.

Sliding scale: Treatment priced by an individual's financial capacity or income. This fee structure exists to help make therapy more affordable for people at a lower income level.

Smart phone apps: A type of software designed to run on a mobile device, such as a smartphone or tablet computer; often referred to as an "app."

Sober social network: A social circle of people who are committed to maintaining sobriety (such as intherooms.com).

Social anxiety: A form of anxiety that is characterized by fear of social situations in which embarrassment or negative evaluation by others can occur. When the anxiety causes a person to suffer significant distress or impairment in functioning, a diagnosis of social anxiety disorder might be warranted.

Social cognition: That part of brain function that allows us to function as individual human beings in a group. It allows us to manage social situations and interact effectively with others. Difficulties with social cognition (such as not understanding subtext or misreading people's motives) occur in a variety of psychiatric disorders, including autism and schizophrenia.

Social Security Disability Insurance (SSDI): A federal insurance program designed to provide income supplements to people who are unable to be employed because of a notable disability; eligible people are required to have a work history and enough credits to qualify.

Social skills training: A rehabilitation service that seeks to improve the functioning of people with SMI by utilizing behavioral techniques to help them acquire interpersonal disease management and independent living skills.

Social withdrawal: A retreat from interpersonal relationships, usually accompanied by an attitude of indifference, detachment, and aloofness. Social withdrawal is often associated with disorders such as schizophrenia, autism, and depression.

Specialized rehabilitation centers: Rehabilitation centers dedicated to psychosocial rehabilitation of people with SMI. These centers also offer opportunities to build social networks.

Stepped care: An important principle when providing care and an intervention is not working (such as when a condition is treatment-resistant to the first-line treatment). In such cases, an algorithm is often used to increase the intensity of care to the next level, such as selecting second- or third-line treatments.

Steroids: A class of medicines used to treat inflammation.

Stigma: A mark or stain that sets someone apart. Stigma can refer to a physical mark (leprosy) or other characteristics (such as having a SMI). Stigma can lead to discrimination and social exclusion.

Stimulant: A medication class that includes amphetamines and methylphenidate (Ritalin).

Stress-vulnerability model: A framework for thinking about the role of rehabilitation services for SMI. This model identifies five key facilitators of recovery: engaging in productive and enjoyable activities; utilizing positive social support; developing effective coping strategies; taking medications; and refraining from use of harmful substances.

Stroke: Also called cerebrovascular accident (CVA), a stroke is a medical emergency that occurs when a part of the brain does not receive blood (ischemic stroke) or if there is bleeding into the brain (hemorrhagic stroke). Symptoms of a stroke include sudden difficulties using a limb or speaking.

Suboxone®: A medication used in maintenance treatment of opioid dependence as part of a comprehensive program that includes counseling and psychological support. Suboxone® is the trade name for buprenorphine in combination with naloxone.

Substance use disorder (SUD): Also called drug addiction, if severe. A SUD is present if someone is unable to control the use of a legal (such as alcohol or nicotine) or illegal substance, with adverse consequences (medical or social) as a result. Craving a substance that leads to loss of control over its use is an important part of an addiction. While it is still commonly used, the term "abuse" is discouraged because it conveys stigma.

Suicide: The act of intentionally killing oneself. Accidents that result in death are not suicide.

Suicide attempt: A survived attempt to kill oneself.

Supplemental Security Income (SSI): Federally funded source of income designed to support aged, blind, and disabled people with little or no income to meet basic needs and to those 65 or older.

Supported education: Individual support and instruction to assist people with psychiatric disorders to achieve their educational goals.

Supported employment and education (SEE): A program designed to help people with psychiatric disorders achieve their vocational and educational goals. This includes working with a SEE specialist to identify career/educational goals and provide needed support to achieve these goals.

Supportive therapy: Treatment designed to improve or sustain a person's well-being and self-esteem.

Sustained symptomatic remission: Remission of symptoms that last for a certain period, usually at least several months.

Symptom: A physical or mental experience that is apparent to the patient and that indicates a condition or disease.

Symptomatic remission: In medicine, the reduction (partial remission) or disappearance (full remission) of symptoms of a disease or disorder.

Syndrome: A group of signs and symptoms that occur together. While the cause and the pathophysiology of a syndrome might be known, such a deep level of understanding is often not present. Most psychiatric disorders are syndromes that are only described at the level of signs and symptoms. Syndromes that look the same can result from very different causes.

Synergistic effects: The interaction or cooperation of two or more organizations or agents to create a greater combined effect than each person can create alone.

Tardive dyskinesia (TD): A late (tardive) complication from the use of antipsychotics that lead to potentially irreversible, characteristic, and abnormal motor movements.

Target protein: Biomolecules that are controlled by biologically-active compounds.

Target symptom: A symptom that is selected as the target of an intervention. Picking (and following its response) the best target symptoms is an important part of treatment planning, particularly when using medications.

Telepsychiatry: A subset of telemedicine, which refers to the delivery of psychiatric services (such as diagnosis and treatment) using technology like videoconferencing.

The Substance Abuse and Mental Health Services Administration (SAMHSA): The substance abuse and mental health services administration within the United States Department of Health and Human Services that leads public health efforts to advance the behavioral health of the nation.

Therapeutic alliance: The relationship between a health care professional and a client to effect beneficial change in the client.

Therapeutic dose: The dose of a medication that is high enough to work. A dose that is too low is called a subtherapeutic dose. It is important to take a therapeutic dose to avoid undertreatment.

Therapeutic drug monitoring (TDM): Measuring the amount of a medication in the blood. TDM can be used to safely use medications or to find the optimal dose. For some medications, TDM is obligatory (such as lithium).

Therapeutic index: A measure of the relative safety of a drug. It compares the dose at which a medication works with the dose that is toxic. Drugs with a narrow therapeutic index, such as lithium, must be carefully dosed to avoid side effects.

Therapeutic misconception: A common error that people who participate in research make and an ethical problem for clinical research. Participants might not fully understand the study goals and design and therefore, greatly overestimate the benefit from participating (and underestimate the risk), including not recognizing that they might receive a placebo.

Therapeutic optimism: A belief in the efficacy of treatment.

Therapist: A broad and imprecise term for a person who provides therapy that is unregulated. Therapists come from a range of backgrounds (such as social work, nursing, or psychology). It is important to learn about somebody's educational training and background before engaging in therapy with a therapist. Therapists often specialize in a one approach (such as a CBT therapist or psychotherapist).

Therapy outcome expectancies: The benefits expected by clients that predict treatment response for cognitive-behavioral therapy.

Third-generation antipsychotic (TGA): A term that is used for antipsychotics that are partial dopamine agonists (and no longer just full-dopamine antagonists) or any of the newest antipsychotics with a more complicated receptor profile. This group of antipsychotics includes aripiprazole, brexpiprazole, and cariprazine.

Third-party payer: A medical insurance term that refers to a party that pays medical bills for a person. Third-party payers include the government (such as Medicaid) or private insurance companies.

Thorazine™: A first-generation antipsychotic drug, also called chlorpromazine.

Thought-behavior-feeling model: A theoretical model underpinning cognitive-behavioral therapy (CBT), which posits that emotions are determined by cognitive appraisals (thoughts).

Thyroid: An endocrine gland in the neck that makes thyroid hormones.

Tics: Lightning-fast, brief, and involuntary movements. Tics, including vocal tics (involuntary utterances), are the hallmark of Tourette syndrome.

Topical: Applied to a body area, usually the skin. Topical medications are often applied as creams or ointments. Topical medications are designed to not reach the bloodstream, which makes them different from transdermal medications, such as those delivered with a patch.

Topiramate (Topamax®): An antiepileptic drug that is also used in psychiatry. As opposed to most psychiatric medications, it causes weight loss.

Torticollis: An involuntary tightening of neck muscles that leads the head to be moved to the side; it is a motor side effect of antipsychotics.

Train and place model: A model of vocational rehabilitation in which a person is trained prior to being placed in a job. It contrasts with a place and train model.

Transcranial magnetic stimulation (TMS): A noninvasive procedure that uses magnetic fields to change neural networks. It is best established for the treatment of depression.

Transdermal: Administration of a drug through the skin, such as through an ointment or an adhesive patch.

Transdermal nicotine patch: A nicotine patch applied to the skin to reduce symptoms of nicotine withdrawal.

Transdiagnostic: Cutting across disease categories. For example, psychosis is a symptom that occurs in a variety of medical, neurological, and psychiatric disorders. Transdiagnostic approaches contrast with categorical approaches.

Transference: A phenomenon within psychotherapy in which the feelings a person had about their parents are unconsciously transferred or redirected to the present situation.

Transinstitutionalization: The moving of people from one institution into another institution. An example from psychiatry is the shifting of patients from a state hospital into the prison system.

Transitional assistance: A government-funded program that provides financial assistance for people that are struggling to make ends meet.

Transitional employment: Temporary paid (often at lower-than-market-value), jobs that are created for clubhouse members.

Traumatic brain injury (TBI): Physical trauma to the head that disrupts the normal function of the brain.

Treatment planning: The deliberate effort to outline steps in treatment for a medical or psychiatric condition, including determining the goals of treatment and the measures and people needed to achieve these goals.

Treatment-resistance: The clinical problem of treatment not working for a disease because of biological factors.

Treatment-resistant depression (TRD): A form of depression in which the biology is such that first-line antidepressants are not working well or at all.

Treatment-resistant schizophrenia (TRS): A form of schizophrenia where the biology is such that first-line antipsychotics are not working well or at all. The antipsychotic clozapine might work in cases of TRS.

Tremor: Involuntary movement or shaking from multiple causes.

Tricyclic antidepressant (TCA) (tricyclic): A class of antidepressants that are older and no longer used routinely. Newer antidepressants are generally better tolerated.

Type I diabetes: A chronic condition in which the pancreas produces little or no insulin, necessitating insulin treatment.

Type II diabetes: The most common form of diabetes that is often associated with obesity and that can be delayed or controlled with diet and exercise. In this form of diabetes, the body does not process blood sugar normally because it does not produce enough insulin and/or there is insulin resistance.

Urgent care clinic: A type of walk-in clinic that focuses on the delivery of care outside of a traditional emergency room.

Urine drug screen: A test using urine to check whether substances were taken. The exact substances tested for depend on the specific test but often include stimulants (such as amphetamine or cocaine), pain medicines (opiates), hallucinogens (phencyclidine), and marijuana (THC).

Valbenazine (Ingrezza®): A VMAT-2 inhibitor to treat tardive dyskinesias.

Valproate: An antiepileptic drug that is also used in psychiatry, mostly as a mood stabilizer.

Valproic acid: Another form of valproate.

Varenicline (Chantix®): A medication used for smoking cessation that reduces craving and the rewarding effects of nicotine.

Virtual reality-assisted therapy: A type of therapy that uses specially programmed computers, visual immersion devices, and artificially created environments to give the patient a simulated experience that can be used to treat psychological conditions.

Virtual reality-based exposure: A type of exposure therapy used to treat anxiety disorders.

Virtual therapy: Therapy that takes place via the phone, an app, a video chat, or even a virtual reality device.

Vivitrol® (naltrexone): A prescription drug used to treat alcohol dependence and prevent opioid dependence and that is given as an injection.

VMAT-2 inhibitors: A class of medications, such as valbenazine and deutetrabenazine, that are used to treat abnormal movements, particularly tardive dyskinesia. The vesicular monoamine transporter 2 (VMAT-2) is presynaptic protein that regulates the release of dopamine from vesicles inside neurons into the synapse.

Vocational rehabilitation: A treatment that helps people with disabilities get and keep a job.

Vocational support agencies: Agencies that support unemployed people who are seeking employment services or job training.

Waist circumference: A biological measure taken around the abdomen at the level of the umbilicus (belly button). The waist circumference can be used to screen patients for possible weight-related health problems, which can indicate the presence of unhealthy fat accumulation inside the abdomen that increases the risk for diabetes.

Withdrawal: A syndrome of physical and psychological symptoms that follows cessation of use or reduction of intake of a psychoactive substance that had been regularly used to induce a state of intoxication.

Working memory: A memory system that allows you to temporarily retain information that you need for something you want to do right now (such as briefly remember a phone number that you want to dial). Working memory is a form of short-term memory. If information needs to be available in the long run, information needs to be moved into long-term memory.

Worry scheduling: A cognitive-behavioral therapy technique based on stimulus control in which a person schedules a specific 30–45 minute period to think about worries and consider solutions. During other parts of the day, the person deliberately avoids thinking about those concerns.

Xerogenic medications: Medications that cause dry mouth.

Yoga: A Hindu spiritual and ascetic discipline, a part of which—including breath control, simple meditation, and the adoption of specific bodily postures—is widely practiced for health and relaxation.

Zero exclusion: The practice of offering supported employment and education to anyone with a SMI. This includes anyone with SMI, not just people who are taking medication or who have been judged "ready" for this service based on symptoms, degree of motivation for work or school, or other factors.

REFERENCES

1. Alia-Klein N, O'Rourke TM, Goldstein RZ, et al: Insight into illness and adherence to psychotropic medications are separately associated with violence severity in a forensic sample. *Aggressive Behavior.* 2007; 33: 86–96.

2. Amador X: *I'm Not Sick and I Don't Need Help.* New York: Vida Press; 2011.

3. Andreasen NC, Carpenter WT, Jr., Kane JM, et al: Remission in schizophrenia: Proposed criteria and rationale for consensus. *American Journal of Psychiatry.* 2005; 162: 441–449.

4. Anthenelli RM, Benowitz NL, West R, et al: Neuropsychiatric safety and efficacy of varenicline, bupropion, and nicotine patch in smokers with and without psychiatric disorders (EAGLES): A double-blind, randomised, placebo-controlled clinical trial. *Lancet.* 2016; 387: 2507–2520.

5. Baldessarini RJ, Vazquez GH, Tondo L: Bipolar depression: A major unsolved challenge. *International Journal of Bipolar Disorders.* 2020; 8: 1.

6. Bartels SJ, Baggett TP, Freudenreich O, et al: COVID-19 emergency reforms in Massachusetts to support behavioral health care and reduce mortality of people with serious mental illness. *Psychiatric Services.* 2020; 71: 1078–1081.

7. Becker DR, Bond GR, Xie H, et al: Job terminations among persons with severe mental illness participating in supported employment. *Community Mental Health Journal.* 1998; 34: 71–82.

8. Beck JS: *Cognitive Therapy for Depression: Basics and Beyond.* 3rd ed., New York: Guilford Press. 2021.

9. Bell IH, Fielding-Smith SF, Hayward M, et al: Smartphone-based ecological momentary assessment and intervention in a blended coping-focused therapy for distressing voices: Development and case illustration. *Internet Intervention.* 2018; 14: 18–25.

10.   Ben-Zeev D, Brenner CJ, Begale M, et al: Feasibility, acceptability, and preliminary efficacy of a smartphone intervention for schizophrenia. *Schizophrenia Bulletin.* 2014; 40: 1244–1253.

11.   Blanchard JJ, Andrea A, Orth RD, et al: Sleep disturbance and sleep-related impairment in psychotic disorders are related to both positive and negative symptoms. *Psychiatry Research.* 2020; 286: 112857. doi: 10.1016/j.psychres.2020.112857. (Epub ahead of print.)

12.   Blanchard JJ, Savage CLG, Orth RD, et al: Sleep problems and social impairment in psychosis: A transdiagnostic study examining multiple social domains. *Frontiers in Psychiatry.* 2020; 11: 486. doi: 10.3389/fpsyt.2020.00486.

13.   Bond GR, Resnick SG, Drake RE, et al: Does competitive employment improve nonvocational outcomes for people with severe mental illness? *Journal of Consulting and Clinical Psychology.* 2001: 489–501.

14.   Bond GR: Supported Employment: Evidence for an Evidence-Based Practice. *Psychiatric Rehabilitation Journal.* 2004; 27: 345–359.

15.   Bourbeau K, Moriarty T, Ayanniyi A, et al: The combined effect of exercise and behavioral therapy for depression and anxiety: Systematic review and meta-analysis. *Behavioral Science (Basel).* 2020; 10(7): 116.

16.   Bradley GM, Couchman GM, Perlesz A, et al: Multiple-family group treatment for English- and Vietnamese-speaking families living with schizophrenia. *Psychiatric Services.* 2006; 57: 1–10.

17.   Burns AMN, Erickson DH, Brenner CA: Cognitive-behavioral therapy for medication-resistant psychosis: A meta-analytic review. *Psychiatric Services.* 2014; 65: 874–880.

18.   Carbon M, Hsieh CH, Kane JM, et al: Tardive dyskinesia prevalence in the period of second-generation antipsychotic use: a meta-analysis. *Journal of Clinical Psychiatry.* 2017; 78: e264–e278.

19.   Constantino MJ, Coyne AE, Boswell JF, et al: A meta-analysis of the association between patients' early perception of treatment credibility and their posttreatment outcomes. *Psychotherapy.* 2018; 55: 486–495.

20.   Cook BL, Wayne GF, Kafali EN, et al: Trends in smoking among adults with mental illness and association between mental health treatment and smoking cessation. *JAMA.* 2014; 311: 172–182.

21.   Cook JA, Copeland ME, Floyd CB, et al: A randomized controlled trial of effects of Wellness Recovery Action Planning on depression, anxiety, and recovery. *Psychiatric Services.* 2012; 63: 541–547.

22. Cook JA, Copeland ME, Jonikas JA, et al: Results of a randomized controlled trial of mental illness self-management using Wellness Recovery Action Planning. *Schizophrenia Bulletin.* 2012; 38: 881–891.

23. Cook JA, Steigman P, Picket S, et al: Randomized controlled trial of peer-led recovery education using Building Recovery of Individual Dreams and Goals through Education and Support (BRIDGES). *Schizophrenia Research.* 2012; 136: 36–42.

24. Copeland M: Wellness Recovery Action Plan. *Occupational Therapy in Mental Health.* 2002; 17(3–4): 127–150.

25. Corigliano V, De Carolis A, Trovini G, et al: Neurocognition in schizophrenia: From prodrome to multi-episode illness. *Psychiatry Research.* 2014; 220: 129–134.

26. Correll CU, Kane JM, Citrome LL: Epidemiology, prevention, and assessment of tardive dyskinesia and advances in treatment. *Journal of Clinical Psychiatry.* 2017; 78: 1136–1147.

27. Correll CU, Rubio JM, Inczedy-Farkas G, et al: Efficacy of 42 pharmacologic cotreatment strategies added to antipsychotic monotherapy in schizophrenia: Systematic overview and quality appraisal of the meta-analytic evidence. *JAMA Psychiatry.* 2017; 74: 675–684.

28. Corrigan PW, Watson AC, Barr L: The self-stigma of mental illness: Implications for self-esteem and self-efficacy. *Journal of Social and Clinical Psychology.* 2006; 25: 875–884.

29. Craig TK, Rus-Calafell M, Ward T, et al: AVATAR therapy for auditory verbal hallucinations in people with psychosis: A single-blind, randomised controlled trial. *The Lancet Psychiatry.* 2018; 5: 31–40.

30. Crowther R, Marshall M, Bond GR, et al: Vocational rehabilitation for people with severe mental illness. *Cochrane Database of Systematic Reviews.* 2001(2): CD003080.

31. Daumit GL, Dickerson FB, Wang N-Y, et al: A behavioral weight-loss intervention in persons with serious mental illness. *New England Journal of Medicine.* 2013; 68: 1594–1602.

32. Deegan PE, Carpenter-Song E, Drake RE, et al: Enhancing clients' communication regarding goals for using psychiatric medications. *Psychiatric Services.* 2017; 68: 771–775.

33. Deegan PE: Recovery and empowerment for people with psychiatric disabilities. *Social Work in Health Care.* 1997; 25: 11–24.

34. Delsignore A, Schnyder U: Control expectancies as predictors of psychotherapy outcome: A systematic review. *British Journal of Clinical Psychology.* 2007; 46: 467–483.

35. Depp CA, Bashem J, Moore RC, et al: GPS mobility as a digital biomarker of negative symptoms in schizophrenia: A case control study. *NPJ Digital Medicine.* 2019; 2: 108.

36. Detore NR, Hintz K, Khare C, et al: Disclosure of mental illness to prospective employers: Clinical, psychosocial, and work correlates in persons receiving supported employment. *Psychiatry Research.* 2019; 273: 312–317.

37. Dickerson F, Schroeder J, Katsafanas E, et al: Cigarette smoking by patients with serious mental illness, 1999–2016: An increasing disparity. *Psychiatric Services.* 2018; 69: 147–153.

38. Dixon L, McFarlane WR, Hornby H, et al: Dissemination of family psychoeducation: The importance of consensus building. *Schizophrenia Research.* 1999; 36: 339.

39. Dixon LB, Lucksted A, Medoff DR, et al: Outcomes of a randomized study of a peer-taught family-to-family education program for mental illness. *Psychiatric Services.* 2011; 62: 591–597.

40. Drake RE, Becker DR: The individual placement and support model of supported employment. *Psychiatric Services.* 1996; 47: 473–475.

41. Dyck DG, Short RA, Hendryx MS, et al: Management of negative symptoms among patients with schizophrenia attending multiple-family groups. *Psychiatric Services.* 2000; 51: 3–9.

42. Eglit GML, Palmer BW, Martin AS, et al: Loneliness in schizophrenia: Construct clarification, measurement, and clinical relevance. *PloS One.* 2018; 13: e0194021.

43. Ekers D, Webster L, Van Straten A, et al: Behavioural activation for depression: An update of meta-analysis of effectiveness and sub group analysis. *PLoS One.* 2014; 9(6): e100100.

44. Emsley R, Rabinowitz J, Medori R: Time course for antipsychotic treatment response in first-episode schizophrenia. *American Journal of Psychiatry.* 2006; 163: 743–745.

45. Estroff SE, Penn DL, Toporek JR: From stigma to discrimination: An analysis of community efforts to reduce the negative consequences of having a psychiatric disorder and label. *Schizophrenia Bulletin.* 2004; 30: 493–509.

46. Fava M: Diagnosis and definition of treatment-resistant depression. *Biological Psychiatry.* 2003; 53: 649–659.

47. Fleury MJ, Grenier G, Bamvita JM, et al: Predictors of quality of life in a longitudinal study of users with severe mental disorders. *Health and Quality of Life Outcomes.* 2011; 11: 92. doi: 10.1186/1477-7525-11-92.

48. Flückiger C, Del AC, Wampold BE, et al: The alliance in adult psychotherapy: A meta-analytic synthesis. *Psychotherapy.* 2018; 55: 316–340.

49. Frankl VE: *Man's Search for Meaning*. Boston, MA: Beacon Press, 1959.

50. Frayne SM, Halanych JH, Miller DR, et al: Disparities in diabetes care: Impact of mental illness. *Archives of Internal Medicine.* 2005; 165: 2631–2638.

51. Freeman D, Haselton P, Freeman J, et al: Automated psychological therapy using immersive virtual reality for treatment of fear of heights: A single-blind, parallel-group, randomised controlled trial. *Lancet Psychiatry.* 2018; 5: 625–632.

52. Freeman D, Taylor KM, Molodynski A, et al: Treatable clinical intervention targets for patients with schizophrenia. *Schizophrenia Research.* 2019; 211: 44–50.

53. Freudenreich O, Cather C: Antipsychotic medication nonadherence: Risk factors and remedies. *Focus.* 2012; 10: 124–129.

54. Freudenreich O, Flaherty AW: Patients with abnormal movements. In: Stern TA, Freudenreich O, Smith FA, et al, eds. *Massachusetts General Handbook of General Hospital Psychiatry*. Philadelphia, PA: Elsevier; 2018. 231–239.

55. Freudenreich O, Holt DJ, Cather C, et al: The evaluation and management of patients with first-episode schizophrenia: A selective, clinical review of diagnosis, treatment, and prognosis. *Harvard Review of Psychiatry.* 2007; 15: 189–211.

56. Freudenreich O, Kontos N, Querques J: Psychiatric polypharmacy: A clinical approach based on etiology and differential diagnosis. *Harvard Review of Psychiatry.* 2012; 20: 79–85.

57. Freudenreich O, Schulz SC, Goff DC: Initial medical work-up of first-episode psychosis: A conceptual review. *Early Intervention in Psychiatry.* 2009; 3: 10–18.

58. Freudenreich O: Differential diagnosis of psychotic symptoms: Medical "mimics": *Psychiatric Times.* 2012 (27)12. Available at: https://www.psychiatrictimes.com/view/differential-diagnosis-psychotic-symptoms-medical-mimics. Accessed February 5, 2021.

59. Freudenreich O: History of schizophrenia care. In: *Psychotic disorders. A Practical Guide,* 2nd ed., Cham, Switzerland: Humana Press, 2020b: 451–464.

60. Freudenreich O: Prevention and clinical staging. In: *Psychotic disorders. A Practical Guide.* 2nd ed., Cham, Switzerland: Humana Press, 2020a: 115–126.

61. Fusar-Poli P, Solmi M, Brondino N, et al: Transdiagnostic psychiatry: A systematic review. *World Psychiatry.* 2019; 18: 192–207.

62. Gaebel W: Status of psychotic disorders in ICD-11. *Schizophrenia Bulletin.* 2012; 38: 895–898.

63. Gerken AT, Baggett TP, Freudenreich O: Consider Rx metformin to prevent metabolic syndrome [Pearls series]. *Current Psychiatry.* 2016; 15: e1–e2.

64. Gillard S: Peer support in mental health services: Where is the research taking us, and do we want to go there? *Journal of Mental Health*. 2018; 28: 341–344.

65. Glenthøj LB, Hjorthøj C, Kristensen TD, et al: The effect of cognitive remediation in individuals at ultra-high risk for psychosis: A systematic review. *NPJ Schizophrenia*. 2017; 3: 1–7.

66. Goff DC, Cather C, Evins AE, et al: Medical morbidity and mortality in schizophrenia: Guidelines for psychiatrists. *Journal of Clinical Psychiatry*. 2005; 66: 183–194.

67. Goff DC, Hill M, Freudenreich O: Treatment adherence in schizophrenia and schizoaffective disorder. *Journal of Clinical Psychiatry*. 2011; 72: e13.

68. Goff DC: Promising evidence of antipsychotic efficacy without dopamine D2–receptor binding. *New England Journal of Medicine*. 2020; 382: 1555–1556.

69. Grant PM, Perivoliotis D, Luther L, et al: Rapid improvement in beliefs, mood, and performance following an experimental success experience in an analogue test of recovery-oriented cognitive therapy. *Psychological Medicine*. 2018; 48: 261–268.

70. Greenberger D, Padesky CA: *Mind Over Mood: A Cognitive Therapy Treatment Manual for Clients*. New York: Guilford Press; 1995.

71. Gross JJ, John OP: Individual differences in two emotion regulation processes: Implications for affect, relationships, and well-being. *Journal of Personality and Social Psychology*. 2003; 85: 348–362.

72. Hall JP, LaPierre TA, Kurth NK: Oral health needs and experiences of Medicaid enrollees with serious mental illness. *American Journal of Preventative Medicine*. 2018; 55: 470–479.

73. Hamann J, Heres S: Adapting shared decision making for individuals with severe mental illness. *Psychiatric Services*. 2014; 65: 1483–1486.

74. Harding CM, Brooks GW, Ashikaga T, et al: The Vermont longitudinal study of persons with severe mental illness, In: Methodology, study sample, and overall status 32 years later. *American Journal of Psychiatry*. 1987; 144: 718–726.

75. Hawton K, Sutton L, Haw C, et al: Schizophrenia and suicide: Systematic review of risk factors. *British Journal of Psychiatry*. 2005; 187: 9–20.

76. Health Resources and Services Administration: The "Loneliness Epidemic." Accessed January 21, 2021, from https://www.hrsa.gov/enews/past-issues/2019/january-17/loneliness-epidemic.

77. Hill M, Freudenreich O: Clozapine: Key discussion points for prescribers. *Clinics in Schizophrenia and Related Psychoses*. 2013; 6: 177–185.

78. Holt-Lunstad J, Smith TB, Baker M, et al: Loneliness and social isolation as risk factors for mortality: A meta-analytic review. *Perspectives in Psychological Sciences.* 2015; 10: 227–237.

79. Hopper K, Wanderling J: Revisiting the developed versus developing country distinction in course and outcome in schizophrenia: Results from ISoS, the WHO collaborative followup project. International Study of Schizophrenia. *Schizophrenia Bulletin.* 2000; 26: 835–846.

80. Howes OD, McCutcheon R, Agid O, et al: Treatment-resistant schizophrenia: Treatment response and resistance in psychosis (TRRIP) Working Group Consensus Guidelines on Diagnosis and Terminology. *American Journal of Psychiatry.* 2017; 174: 216–229.

81. Huhn M, Nikolakopoulou A, Schneider-Thoma J, et al: Comparative efficacy and tolerability of 32 oral antipsychotics for the acute treatment of adults with multi-episode schizophrenia: A systematic review and network meta-analysis. *Lancet.* 2019; 394: 939–951.

82. Hu MX, Turner D, Generaal E, et al: Exercise interventions for the prevention of depression: A systematic review of meta-analyses. *BMC Public Health.* 2020; 8; 20(1): 1255.

83. Hwong A, Wang K, Bent S, et al: Breast cancer screening in women with schizophrenia: A systematic review and meta-analysis. *Psychiatric Services.* 2020; 71: 263–268.

84. Jacquart J, Dutcher CD, Freeman SZ, et al: The effects of exercise on transdiagnostic treatment targets: A meta-analytic review. *Behavioral Research Therapy.* 2019; 115: 19–37.

85. Javitt DC: Is the glycine site half saturated or half unsaturated? Effects of glutamatergic drugs in schizophrenia patients. *Current Opinion in Psychiatry.* 2006; 19: 151–157.

86. Jha P, Ramasundarahettige C, Landsman V, et al: 21st-century hazards of smoking and benefits of cessation in the United States. *New England Journal of Medicine.* 2013; 368: 341–350.

87. Johnson S, Lamb D, Marston L, et al: Peer-supported self- management for people discharged from a mental health crisis team: A randomised controlled trial. *Lancet.* 2018; 392: 409–418.

88. Joiner TE: *Why People Die by Suicide.* Cambridge, MA: Harvard University Press; 2005.

89. Kane JM, Agid O, Baldwin ML, et al: Clinical guidance on the identification and management of treatment-resistant schizophrenia. *Journal of Clinical Psychiatry.* 2019; 80: pii: 18com12123.

90. Kane JM, Robinson DG, Schooler NR, et al: Comprehensive versus usual community care for first-episode psychosis: 2-year outcomes from the NIMH RAISE Early Treatment Program. *American Journal of Psychiatry.* 2015; 173: 362–372.

91. Kane JM, Schooler NR, Marcy P, et al: The RAISE early treatment program for first-episode psychosis: Background, rationale, and study design. *Journal of Clinical Psychiatry.* 2015; 76: 240–246.

92. Kessler RC, Barker PR, Colpe LJ, et al: Screening for serious mental illness in the general population. *Archives of General Psychiatry.* 2003; 60: 184–189.

93. Kisely S, Baghaie H, Laloo R, et al: A systematic review and meta-analysis of the association between poor oral health and severe mental illness. *Psychosomatic Medicine.* 2015; 77: 83–92.

94. Kishimoto T, Robenzadeh A, Leucht C, et al: Long-acting injectable vs oral antipsychotics for relapse prevention in schizophrenia: A meta-analysis of randomized trials. *Schizophrenia Bulletin.* 2014; 40: 192–213.

95. Krabbendam L, Aleman A: Cognitive rehabilitation in schizophrenia: A quantitative analysis of controlled studies. *Psychopharmacology (Berl).* 2003; 169: 376–382.

96. Kreyenbuhl J, Nossel IR, Dixon LB: Disengagement from mental health treatment among individuals with schizophrenia and strategies for facilitating connections to care: A review of the literature. *Schizophrenia Bulletin.* 2009; 35: 696–703.

97. Kurtz MM, Mueser KT: A meta-analysis of controlled research on social skills training for schizophrenia. *Journal of Consulting and Clinical Psychology.* 2008; 76: 491–504.

98. Kübler-Ross E: *On Death and Dying.* New York, NY: Macmillan; 1969.

99. Lally J, Ajnakina O, Di Forti M, et al: Two distinct patterns of treatment resistance: Clinical predictors of treatment resistance in first-episode schizophrenia spectrum psychoses. *Psychological Medicine.* 2016; 46: 3231–3240.

100. Lally J, Tully J, Robertson D, et al: Augmentation of clozapine with electroconvulsive therapy in treatment resistant schizophrenia: A systematic review and meta-analysis. *Schizophrenia Research.* 2016; 171: 215–224.

101. Lambert M, Naber D, Schacht A, et al: Rates and predictors of remission and recovery during 3 years in 392 never-treated patients with schizophrenia. *Acta Psychiatrica Scandanavia.* 2008; 118: 220–229.

102. Leucht S, Tardy M, Komossa K, et al: Antipsychotic drugs versus placebo for relapse prevention in schizophrenia: A systematic review and meta-analysis. *Lancet.* 2012; 379: 2063–2071.

103. Lindenmayer JP, Kulsa MKC, Sultana T, et al: Transcranial direct-current stimulation in ultra-treatment-resistant schizophrenia. *Brain Stimulation.* 2019; 12: 54–61.

104. Lubman DI, Velakoulis D, McGorry PD, et al: Incidental radiological findings on brain magnetic resonance imaging in first-episode psychosis and chronic schizophrenia. *Acta Psychiatrica Scandinavica.* 2002; 106: 331–336.

105. Mangurian C, Newcomer JW, Modlin C, et al: Diabetes and cardiovascular care among people with severe mental illness: A literature review. *Journal of General Internal Medicine.* 2016; 31: 1083–1091.

106. Marmot M, Friel S, Bell R, et al; Commission on social determinants of health: Closing the gap in a generation: Health equity through action on the social determinants of health. *Lancet.* 2008; 372: 1661–1669.

107. McFarlane WR, Cook WL: Family expressed emotion prior to onset of psychosis. *Family Process.* 2007; 46: 185–197.

108. McGorry PD, Nelson B, Markulev C, et al: Effect of omega-3 polyunsaturated fatty acids in young people at ultrahigh risk for psychotic disorders: The NEURAPRO randomized clinical trial. *JAMA Psychiatry.* 2017; 74: 19–27.

109. McGurk SR, Twamley EW, Sitzer DI, et al: A meta-analysis of cognitive remediation in schizophrenia. *American Journal of Psychiatry.* 2007; 164: 1791–802.

110. McIntyre RS, Kennedy SH, Soczynska JK, et al: Attention-deficit/hyperactivity disorder in adults with bipolar disorder or major depressive disorder: Results from the international mood disorders collaborative project. *Prim Care Companion J Clin Psychiatry.* 2010; 12(3).

111. Meagher DJ, Moran M, Raju B, et al: Phenomenology of delirium. Assessment of 100 adult cases using standardised measures. *British Journal of Psychiatry.* 2007; 190: 135–141.

112. Miller BJ, Goldsmith DR: Towards an immunophenotype of schizophrenia: progress, potential mechanisms, and future directions. *Neuropsychopharmacology.* 2017; 42: 299–317.

113. Miller BJ, Parker CB, Rapaport MH, et al: Insomnia and suicidal ideation in nonaffective psychosis. *Sleep.* 2019; 42: zsy215.

114. Miller DD: Review and management of clozapine side effects. *Journal of Clinical Psychiatry.* 2000; 61 Suppl 8: 14–17.

115. Mittelmark MB, Sagy S, Eriksson M, et al, eds.: *The Handbook of Salutogenesis*. Cham, Switzerland: Springer; 2017.

116. Morrison AP, Pyle M, Maughan D, et al: Antipsychotic medication versus psychological intervention versus a combination of both in adolescents with first-episode psychosis (MAPS): A multicentre, three-arm, randomised controlled pilot and feasibility study. *Lancet Psychiatry*. 2020; 7(9): 788–800.

117. Mueser KT, DeTore NR, Kredlow MA, et al: Clinical and demographic correlates of stigma in first-episode psychosis: The impact of duration of untreated psychosis. *Acta Psychiatrica Scandinavica*. 2020; 141: 157–166.

118. Mueser KT, Glynn SM: *Behavioral Family Therapy for Psychiatric Disorders*. 2nd ed., Oakland, CA: New Harbinger, 1999.

119. Mueser KT, Penn DL, Addington J, et al: The NAVIGATE Program for First-Episode Psychosis: Rationale, overview, and description of psychosocial components. *Psychiatric Services*. 2015; 66: 680–690.

120. Murthy VH: *Together: The Healing Power of Human Connection in a Sometimes Lonely World*. New York, NY: Harper Wave; 2020.

121. Myers E, Startup H, Freeman D: Cognitive behavioural treatment of insomnia in individuals with persistent persecutory delusions: A pilot trial. *Journal of Behavior and Therapeutic Experimental Psychiatry*. 2011; 42: 330–336.

122. Ng QX, Soh AYS, Venkatanarayanan N, et al: A systematic review of the effect of probiotic supplementation on schizophrenia symptoms. *Neuropsychobiology*. 2019; 78: 1–6.

123. Olfson M, Gerhard T, Huang C, et al: Premature mortality among adults with schizophrenia in the United States. *JAMA Psychiatry*. 2015; 72: 1172–1181.

124. Osborn DP, Wright CA, Levy G, et al: Relative risk of diabetes, dyslipidaemia, hypertension and the metabolic syndrome in people with severe mental illnesses: systematic review and metanalysis. *BMC Psychiatry*. 2008; 8: 84.

125. Oyebode F: *Sims' Symptoms In the Mind: Textbook of Descriptive Psychopathology*. Philadelphia: Elsevier; 2018.

126. Papakostas GI, Shelton RC, Zajecka JM, et al: Effect of adjunctive L-methylfolate 15 mg among inadequate responders to SSRIs in depressed patients who were stratified by biomarker levels and genotype: Results from a randomized clinical trial. *Journal of Clinical Psychiatry*. 2014; 75(8): 855–863.

127. Paudel S, Brown H, Freudenreich O: The neurobiology of schizoaffective disorder. *Psychiatric Annals*. 2020; 50: 190–194.

128. Pilling S, Bebbington P, Kuipers E, et al: Psychological treatments in schizophrenia: II. Meta-analyses of randomized controlled trials of social skills training and cognitive remediation. *Psychological Medicine*. 2002; 32: 783–791.

129. Pot-Kolder RMCA, Geraets CNW, Veling W, et al: Virtual-reality-based cognitive behavioural therapy versus waiting list control for paranoid ideation and social avoidance in patients with psychotic disorders: A single-blind randomized controlled trial. *Lancet Psychiatry*. 2018; 5: 217–226.

130. Prochaska JJ: Smoking and mental illness—breaking the link. *New England Journal of Medicine*. 2011; 365: 196–198.

131. Ritsher JB, Otilingam PG, Grajales M: Internalized stigma of mental illness: Psychometric properties of a new measure. *Psychiatry Research*. 2003; 121: 31–49.

132. Roffman JL, Petruzzi LJ, Tanner AS, et al: Biochemical, physiological and clinical effects of l-methylfolate in schizophrenia: A randomized controlled trial. *Molecular Psychiatry*. 2018; 23: 316–322.

133. SAMHSA: The CBHSQ Report. Accessed July 20, 2017, from https://www.samhsa.gov/data/sites/default/files/report_3190/ShortReport-3190.html.

134. Sandhu KV, Sherwin E, Schellekens H, et al: Feeding the microbiota-gut-brain axis: Diet, microbiome, and neuropsychiatry. *Translational Research*. 2017; 179: 223–244.

135. Schane RE, Ling, PM, Glantz SA: Health effects of light and intermittent smoking: A review. *Circulation*. 2010; 121: 1518–1522.

136. Schildbach S, Schildbach C: Criminalization through transinstitutionalization: A critical review of the Penrose hypothesis in the context of compensation imprisonment. *Frontiers in Psychiatry*. 2018; 9: 534.

137. Schoretsanitis G, Kane JM, Correll CU, et al, for the ASCP and TDM task force of AGNP: Blood levels to optimize antipsychotic treatment in clinical practice; a joint consensus of the American Society of Clinical Psychopharmacology (ASCP) and the therapeutic drug monitoring (TDM) task force of the Arbeitsgemeinschaft für Neuropsychopharmakologie und Pharmakopsychiatrie (AGNP). *Journal of Clinical Psychiatry*. 2020; 81: 19cs13169. doi: 10.4088/JCP.19cs13169.

138. Schuling R, Huijbers MJ, van Ravesteijn H, et al: Recovery from recurrent depression: Randomized controlled trial of the efficacy of mindfulness-based compassionate living compared with treatment-as-usual on depressive symptoms and its consolidation at longer term follow-up. *Journal of Affective Disorders*. 2020; 273: 265–273.

139. Seligman MEP, Steen TA, Park N, et al: Positive psychology progress: Empirical validation of interventions. *American Psychologist*. 2005; 60(5): 410–421.

140. Sheffield JM, Karcher NR, Barch DM: Cognitive deficits in psychotic disorders: A lifespan perspective. *Neuropsychology Review.* 2018; 28: 509–533.

141. Sisti DA, Segal AG, Emanuel EJ: Improving long-term psychiatric care: Bring back the asylum. *JAMA.* 2015; 313: 243–244.

142. Soares-Weiser K, Maayan N, Bergman H: Vitamin E for antipsychotic-induced tardive dyskinesia. *Cochrane Database of Systematic Reviews.* 2018; 1: CD000209.

143. Solmi M, Pigato G, Kane JM, et al: Treatment of tardive dyskinesia with VMAT-2 inhibitors: A systematic review and meta-analysis of randomized controlled trials. *Drug Design, Development and Therapy.* 2018; 12: 1215–1238.

144. Stonerock GL, Hoffman BL, Smith PJ, et al: Exercise as treatment for anxiety: Systematic review and analysis. *Annals of Behavioral Medicine.* 2015; 49(4): 542–556.

145. Subotnik KL, Casaus LR, Ventura J, et al: Long-acting injectable risperidone for relapse prevention and control of breakthrough symptoms after a recent first episode of schizophrenia. A randomized clinical trial. *JAMA Psychiatry.* 2015; 72: 822–829.

146. Subramaniam M, Abdin E, Shahwan S, et al: Prevalence, correlates and outcomes of insomnia in patients with first episode psychosis from a tertiary psychiatric institution in Singapore. *General Hospital Psychiatry.* 2018; 51: 15–21.

147. Taipale H, Mittendorfer-Rutz E, Alexanderson K, et al: Antipsychotics and mortality in a nationwide cohort of 29,823 patients with schizophrenia. *Schizophrenia Research.* 2018; 197: 274–280.

148. Teasdale SB, Ward PB, Samaras K, et al: Dietary intake of people with severe mental illness: Systematic review and meta-analysis. *British Journal of Psychiatry.* 2019; 214: 251–259.

149. Teixeira C, Mueser KT, Rogers ES, et al: Job endings and work trajectories of persons receiving supported employment and cognitive remediation. *Psychiatric Services.* 2018; 69: 812–818.

150. Torous J, Keshavan M: COVID-19, mobile health and serious mental illness. *Schizophrenia Research.* 2020; doi:10.1016/S2215–0366(17)30427–3.

151. Tuesley KM, Jordan SJ, Siskind DJ, et al: Colorectal, cervical and prostate cancer screening in Australians with severe mental illness: Retrospective nation-wide cohort study. *Australian and New Zealand Journal of Psychiatry.* 2019; 53: 550–558.

152. Valiente C, Espinosa R, Trucharte A, et al: The challenge of well-being and quality of life: A meta-analysis of psychological interventions in schizophrenia. *Schizophrenia Research.* 2019; 208: 16–24.

153. Velligan DI, Bow-Thomas CC, Huntzinger C, et al: Randomized controlled trial of the use of compensatory strategies to enhance adaptive functioning in outpatients with schizophrenia. *American Journal of Psychiatry.* 2000; 157: 1317–1323.

154. Vermeulen JM, van Rooijen G, van de Kerkhof MPJ, et al: Clozapine and long-term mortality risk in patients with schizophrenia: A systematic review and meta-analysis of studies lasting 1.1–12.5 Years. *Schizophrenia Bulletin.* 2019; 45: 315–329.

155. Volavka J, Vevera J: Very long-term outcome of schizophrenia. *International Journal of Clinical Practice.* 2018; 72: e13094.

156. Wehmeyer ML, Palmer SB: Adult outcomes for students with cognitive disabilities three-years after high school: The impact of self-determination. *Education and Training in Developmental Disabilities.* 2003; 38: 131–144.

157. Weiner RD, Reti IM: Key updates in the clinical application of electroconvulsive therapy. *International Review of Psychiatry.* 2017; 29: 54–62.

158. Wenzel A, Jager-Hyman S: Cognitive therapy for suicidal patients: Current status. *Behavior Therapy.* 2012; 35: 121–130.

159. Williams R, Malla A, Roy MA, et al: What is the place of clozapine in the treatment of early psychosis in Canada? *Canadian Journal of Psychiatry.* 2017; 62: 109–114.

160. World Health Organization: The World Health Organization Quality of Life (WHOQOL). Accessed January 21, 2021, from https://www.who.int/mental_health/publications/whoqol/en/.

161. Zipursky RB, Reilly TJ, Murray RM: The myth of schizophrenia as a progressive brain disease. *Schizophrenia Bulletin.* 2013; 39: 1363–1372.

162. Zohar J, Kasper S: Neuroscience-based Nomenclature (NbN): A call for action. *The World Journal of Biological Psychiatry.* 2016; 17: 318–320.

163. Zubin J, Spring B: Vulnerability: A new view of schizophrenia. *Journal of Abnormal Psychology.* 1977; 86: 103–126.

Suggested Resources

Workbooks

1. Barlow DH, Craske MG: *Mastery of Your Anxiety and Panic: Workbook.* 4th ed., New York: Oxford University Press; 2005.

2. CBT and DBT psychoeducation, exercises, and worksheets: Centre for Clinical Interventions-Western Australia. Accessed January 21, 2021, from https://www.cci. health.wa.gov.au/Resources/Overview.

3. Greenberger D, Padesky CA: *Mind Over Mood: A Cognitive Therapy Treatment Manual for Clients.* New York: Guilford Press; 1995.

4. Hope DA, Heimberg RG, Turk CL: *Managing Social Anxiety: A Cognitive-Behavioral Therapy Approach.* 2nd ed., New York: Oxford University Press; 2010.

5. Linehan M: *DBT Skills Training Handouts and Worksheets.* New York: The Guilford Press; 2015.

INDEX

A

Abnormal Involuntary Movement Scale (AIMS), 56
activity, 127, 132, 135–136
advance directives, 140
alcohol use, 26, 125–126
alternative treatments, 98–99
anger, 105, 116, 123–124, 149
antidepressants, 48–49, 94, 148
antipsychotics, 48–51, 53–59, 92–93, 95, 99, 148
anxiolytics, 48, 50
Assertive Community Treatment (ACT), 109
attention deficit disorder (ADD), 32
attention deficit hyperactivity disorder (ADHD), 85–86

B

behavioral activation (BA), 119–120
bipolar disorder
    characteristics and definition of, 5–6
    co-morbid conditions, 32, 85
    diagnosis, 32
    disclosing diagnosis of, 111
    finding experienced therapists, 74
    health problems associated with, 130
    individual therapy for, 64–66
    interpersonal social rhythm therapy for, 72

long-acting injectable medications for, 58–59
    mood stabilizers for, 48–49
    prognosis, 144, 146, 148
    psychotropic medications for, 48, 56, 95
    relapse prevention, 39
    talk therapy and, 44
    treatment goals, 38–42, 93–95
brain imaging/brain scans, 30–31

C

cannabis, 5, 26, 30, 33
carbamazepine, 49, 56–57
chronic depression
    characteristics and definition of, 6
    diagnosis, 32
    electroconvulsive therapy for, 97–98
    treatment, 48
    treatment-resistant, 94–95
clinical interviews, 5, 27–28, 32
clinical trials, 100–101, 111–112
clozapine, 50–51, 54, 57, 96–97
clubhouses, 80–81, 88–89
cognitive difficulties, 85, 92, 145
collateral information, 17, 27, 32
contingency management, 20
coping skills, 108–109, 116–127
core symptoms, 4, 51, 65, 94
coronavirus pandemic, 9
crisis plans, 107–108

Made in United States
North Haven, CT
23 October 2021

10536644R00134